A GUIDE to the

Woody Plants of Colorado

by GEORGE W. KELLY

A GUIDE to the

Woody Plants of Colorado

by GEORGE W. KELLY

PRUETT PUBLISHING COMPANY
Boulder, Colorado 80302

CCD-A

Library of Congress Catalog Card Number 77-114006

Printed in the United States of America

In Appreciation:

It would not have been possible to bring this book to life without the wonderful photographs given me many years ago by Charles J. Ott and R.J. Niedrach. All photographs not otherwise credited are by the author.

This book was lithographed on 60# Boise Cascade offset book, with a 10 point Celex cover from Appleton Mills. The map was lithographed on 80# Mead AcroArt, a washable plastic from Mead Paper Company. The text is set in Times Roman with Trade Gothic cutlines. Map call-outs are Times Roman bold, Goudy bold italic, and Univers, with Schoolbook heads. Design and lithography by Pruett Press, Incorporated, Boulder, Colorado.

Contents

Foreword

This work, *The Woody Plants Of Colorado*, is the result of tireless field investigations by George W. Kelly and his wife, Sue, over a period of many years, and the undersigned has been privileged to accompany them on botanical researches in many parts of Colorado.

George Kelly is a dedicated field man, botanist and gardener. He has written columns on gardening for numerous publications, and his book, *Rocky Mountain Horticulture*, is a classic needed by all who have attempted to raise flowers, shrubs, and trees in states of little rainfall.

He edited the *Green Thumb*, now the official publication of the Denver Botanic Garden, and was a commentator for many years on KOA and KLZ of Denver. He was the horticulturist for the Colorado Forestry and Horticulture Association and Mile High Horticulturist. In recognition for his public service in promoting horticulture and beauty, he has received numerous honors from the American Horticultural Council (1957), the Federation of Garden Clubs, and the Colorado Nurserymen's Association (1966), as well as the Johnny Appleseed award from the Men's Garden Clubs (1955) and the "Man of the Year" award from the City of Cortez, Colorado (1968). Actively interested in the welfare of young people, George Kelly and I worked in scouting in early days, and were co-founders of the Junior Mountain Club. He is adept as an artist with camera, stonework, or the spoken word; the first stanza of his poem, *Beauty*, opposite the title page of his garden book rather nicely sums up George's philosophy of life:

> Beauty is where we find it.
> Sure it may be in sunset glow,
> Or it may be in flowers or birds or trees.
> We'll find it wherever we go.

The present work, covering the trees and shrubs of Colorado, is a result of a lifetime of study in this state with its wide range of elevation, from the plains of the upper sonoran zone, upward through the various life zones to the alpine summits of our mighty mountains. All of us interested in botany owe a debt of gratitude to the author, George W. Kelly, for his latest publication.

Robert J. Niedrach
DENVER MUSEUM OF NATURAL HISTORY

Preface

The Why and How of This Book

The idea probably started many years ago, when I worked with M. Walter Pesman, and hiked the hills with R.J. Niedrach. I wanted to know the name and character of every plant I saw. I found few people who knew the plants, and the only books on the subject were difficult to work with.

When I got a copy of Professor B.O. Longyear's book, *Trees and Shrubs of the Rocky Mountain Region*, I thought it was the most valuable book I had ever owned. I practically memorized it verbatim. Since then I have been associating with the native plants of Colorado whenever possible, acquiring a personal knowledge of them. I was always especially interested in the shrubs.

Ten years ago, Bob Niedrach suggested that I put down on paper many of the things I had learned about the native shrubs of Colorado, and said he would supply the necessary pictures. I worked up the text, and Bob experimented with photography until he had worked out a system of making really good black and white portraits of the shrubs. I had acquired a rather complete library of colored slides, but we did not see how we could finance the printing of many pictures in color. However, the pressure of Bob's work became such that he was unable to finish the black and white series, so the book lay dormant for several years.

Just recently it came to my attention that the color approach might not be impossible after all, so I put my original notes and yearly revisions into shape for publication.

The descriptions are largely from personal observations *in the field*, and take note of the outstanding characteristics of each plant which separate it from every other plant. Much data is given, describing the old-time uses of each plant, as well as its practical application to current methods of landscaping. In addition, an entirely new and different method of identification is used. I believe that the book, for all its down-to-earthness, is still scientifically correct. We hope that it will help you to become better acquainted with the "natives," and in so doing, enable you to derive more pleasure and satisfaction from every visit to this vast wonderland of nature that is Colorado.

Why This Book Is Needed

There are several other books, mentioned in the bibliography, that give information on native Colorado shrubs and other woody plants. Some are incomplete, others are out of date, and most require much botanical knowledge to be able to identify a plant. This book is based on characteristics as seen in the field, and also gives many uses of these plants, both ancient and modern. Actual photographs will help in identification.

How To Use This Book

If you find an unknown shrub, first locate its approximate altitude and general location on the map. Then note its habitat, as to sun and moisture, then its average size. Finally, note its leaves, flowers, fruit, stem, and any unusual or outstanding characteristics such as bright-red bark, fern-like leaves, or tiny flowers. Now, referring to the altitude charts you will probably find one plant that fits all these specifications. Then refer to the page indicated for details and verification of your guess. If your first guess does not check, try again. This process should be much quicker and simpler than running a typical botanical key. Nomenclature used here has been checked to conform in most cases with that used by Dr. H.D. Harrington in his *Manual of the Plants of Colorado*.

Common Names

Descriptions of these plants are under their botanical names.

Adam's Needle—*Yucca*
Adelia—*Forestiera*
Almáciga de Sabina—*Juniperus*
Alder—*Alnus*
Algerita-berry—*Rhamnus*
Antelope-brush—*Purshia*
Apache Plume—*Fallugia*
Aromatic Sumac—*Rhus*
Ash—*Fraxinus*
Aspen—*Populus*
Aster—*Aster*
Azalea—*Rhododendron*
Barberry—*Berberis*
Bearberry—*Arctostaphylos, Lonicera*
Bilberry—*Vaccinium*
Birch—*Betula*
Bird Cherry—*Prunus*
Bitterbrush—*Purshia*
Blackbrush—*Coleogyne*
Blueberry—*Vaccinium*
Boxelder—*Acer*
Boxleaf—*Pachystima*
Brickellbush—*Brickellia*
Brigham Tea—*Ephedra*
Brownweed—*Gutierrezia*
Buckbrush—*Symphoricarpos*
Buckthorn—*Rhamnus*
Buckwheat—*Eriogonum*
Buffaloberry—*Shepherdia*
Bundle Flower—*Desmanthus*
Cactus—*Echinocereus, Opuntia, Echinocactus, Mamillaria*
Capulín Silvestre—*Sambucus*
Cat's Claws—*Mimosa*
Cedar—*Juniperus*
Chamiso—*Artemisia, Atriplex*
Chamiso Blanco—*Chrysothamnus*
Cherry—*Prunus*
Chico—*Lycium*
Chinaberry—*Sapindus*
Chokecherry—*Prunus*

1

Cholla—*Opuntia*
Cinquefoil—*Potentilla*
Clematis—*Clematis*
Cliffbush—*Jamesia*
Cliffrose—*Cowania*
Compass Plant—*Echinocactus*
Copperweed—*Oxytenia*
Coralberry—*Symphoricarpos*
Cottonwood—*Populus*
Creambush—*Holodiscus*
Creosote Bush—*Larrea* (*Covillea*)
Currant—*Ribes*
Dátil—*Yucca*
Desert Broom—*Baccharis*
Desert Rue—*Thamnosma*
Desert-thorn—*Lycium*
Devil's Claw—*Echinocactus*
Dogwood—*Cornus*
Douglas Fir—*Pseudotsuga*
Dryad—*Dryas*
Dunebroom—*Parryella*
Elder—*Sambucus*
False Azalea—*Rhododendron*
False Indigo—*Amorpha*
False Juniper—*Leptodactylon*
False Mockorange—*Fendlera*
Featherbush—*Cercocarpus*
Feather-rose—*Fallugia*
Felt-thorn—*Tetradymia*
Fendlerbush—*Fendlera, Fendlerella*
Fernbush—*Chamaebatiaria*
Filbert—*Corylus*
Fir—*Abies*
Frostweed—*Helianthemum*
Goldenbush—*Chrysothamnus*
Goldenweed—*Haplopappus*
Gooseberry—*Ribes*
Grape—*Vitis*
Greasebush—*Forsellesia*
Greasewood—*Sarcobatus*
Groundsel—*Senecio*
Groundsel Tree—*Baccharis*
Grouseberry—*Vaccinium*
Hackberry—*Celtis*

Hawthorn—*Crataegus*
Hazel-nut—*Corylus*
Heath—*Phyllodoce*
Heather—*Phyllodoce*
Hediondilla—*Larrea*
Holly-grape—*Berberis*
Honeysuckle—*Lonicera*
Hop-sage—*Grayia*
Hoptree—*Ptelea*
Horsebrush—*Tetradymia*
Huckleberry—*Vaccinium*
Hydrangea—*Jamesia*
Indian Banana—*Yucca*
Indian Currant—*Symphoricarpos*
Jointfir—*Ephedra*
Juneberry—*Amelanchier*
Juniper—*Juniperus*
King's Crown—*Echinocereus*
Kinnikinnick—*Arctostaphylos*
Laurel—*Kalmia*
Leadplant—*Amorpha*
Lemonade Sumac—*Rhus*
Locust—*Robinia*
Mahonia—*Berberis*
Manzanita—*Arctostaphylos*
Maple—*Acer*
Matrimony Vine—*Lycium*
Meadowsweet—*Holodiscus*
Mesquite—*Prosopis*
Mistletoe—*Loranthaceae* (*Arceuthobium, Phoradendron*)
Mockheather—*Frankenia*
Mockorange—*Philadelphus*
Mooseberry—*Viburnum*
Mormon Tea—*Ephedra*
Mountain Ash—*Sorbus*
Mountain Avens—*Dryas*
Mountain Balm—*Ceanothus*
Mountain Laurel—*Kalmia*
Mountain Lover—*Pachystima*
Mountain Mahogany—*Cercocarpus*
Mountain Mockorange—*Jamesia*
Mountain Privet—*Forestiera*
Mountain Spray—*Holodiscus*
Nail Wort—*Paronychia*

Nannyberry—*Viburnum*
New Jersey Tea—*Ceanothus*
Ninebark—*Physocarpus*
Oak—*Quercus*
Oldman—*Senecio*
Orache—*Atriplex*
Oregon-grape—*Berberis*
Palo Blanco—*Forestiera*
Palo Duro—*Cercocarpus*
Pin Cherry—*Prunus*
Pine—*Pinus*
Pipsissewa—*Chimaphila*
Plum—*Prunus*
Poison Ivy—*Rhus*
Poñil—*Fallugia*
Poplar—*Populus*
Prickly Pear—*Opuntia*
Quaking Aspen—*Populus*
Quininebush—*Cowania*
Rabbit Brush—*Chrysothamnus*
Raspberry—*Rubus*
Redbud—*Cercis*
Redroot—*Ceanothus*
Rigidplume—*Oxytenia*
Rockmat—*Spiraea*
Rock Spirea—*Holodiscus*
Rose—*Rosa*
Rosemary Mint—*Poliomintha*
Rubber Shrub—*Chrysothamnus*
Russia Olive—*Elaeagnus*
Rustyleaf—*Menziesia*
Sagebrush—*Artemisia*
Salmonberry—*Rubus*
Saltbrush—*Atriplex*
Salt Cedar—*Tamarix*
Sand Cherry—*Prunus*
Seablite—*Suaeda*
Seepweed—*Suaeda*
Seepwillow—*Baccharis*
Service-berry—*Amelanchier*
Shadbush—*Amelanchier*
Silverleaf—*Shepherdia*
Skunkbrush—*Rhus*
Snakeweed—*Gutierrezia*

4

Snowberry—*Symphoricarpos*
Soapberry—*Sapindus*
Soapweed—*Yucca*
Spanish Bayonet—*Yucca*
Spirea—*Spiraea*
Spruce—*Picea*
Squashberry—*Viburnum*
Squaw Apple—*Peraphyllum*
Squawbush—*Rhus*
Sumac—*Rhus*
Tamarisk—*Tamarix*
Tanglebrush—*Forestiera*
Tansybush—*Chamaebatiaria*
Thicket Creeper—*Parthenocissus*
Thimbleberry—*Rubus*
Thoroughwort—*Brickellia*
Threeleaf-sumac—*Rhus*
Turpentine-broom—*Thamnosma*
Turpentine-weed—*Gutierrezia*
Twinflower—*Linnaea*
Umbrella Plant—*Eriogonum*
Virgin's Bower—*Clematis*
Virginia Creeper—*Parthenocissus*
Wafer Ash—*Ptelea*
Waterwillow—*Baccharis*
Waxflower—*Jamesia*
White Sage—*Eurotia*
Whitlow-wort—*Paronychia*
Whortleberry—*Vaccinium*
Willow—*Salix*
Winterfat—*Eurotia*
Wintergreen—*Gaultheria*
Wolfberry—*Lycium, Symphoricarpos*
Woodbine—*Parthenocissus*
Yedra—*Rhus*
Yerba de la Sangre—*Berberis*

Glossary

anther:	the pollen-bearing structure at the end of the stamen
axillary:	in the axis, as with lateral, or axillary buds
"bloom":	the waxy coating over a surface, as on leaves or fruit, often whitish
bract:	the modified leaves present usually at the base of a flower
calyx:	the whorl of modified "leaves" immediately outward from the petals of a flower
chlorosis:	diseased condition in plants shown by the blanching of green parts
cyme:	a flat-topped or convex flower cluster of determinate growth; central flowers are the first to mature
exserted:	extending beyond the surrounding organ
fascicle:	a dense bundle or cluster
filiform:	having the shape of a thread or filament
floccose:	having scattered, loose tufts of wool-like hair
glabrous:	smooth, no hairs present
glaucous:	coated by a waxy layer, usually whitish, which usually rubs off readily
involucre:	a whorl of leaves just below a flower or inflorescence
lanceolate:	narrow leaf, broadest toward the base. Lance-shaped, about 5 times as long as wide
lenticels:	cortical pores in the stems of woody plants
linear:	narrow leaf having parallel sides; about 6-15 times as long as wide
node:	place along the stem where leaves, buds or branch stems arise
obovate:	opposite of ovate in being broadest near the apex
ovate:	egg-shaped with the broadest area toward the base
palmate:	leaves in which the midribs come together at their base
panicle:	flower cluster in which individual flowers are on branched stalks
persistent:	remaining attached; not falling off
petiole:	stalk of a leaf attaching the blade to the stem
pinnate:	arranged with leaflets or veins arising at opposite sides of a central axis

pinnatifid:	lobed or cleft with sinuses extending more than halfway to the midrib
pistillate:	furnished with a pistil or pistils, the ovule-bearing organ of a seed plant
pith:	the spongy center of a stem, interior to the vascular bundles and wood
procumbent:	growing along the ground but not rooting or turning up
propagate:	to cause to continue or multiply by generation; to cause to spread or disseminate; to transmit
pubescent:	being covered with hairs, particularly with short soft hairs
reflexed:	turned abruptly downward or backward
restricted:	limited or confined parts of plants
saponin:	any of a group of glucosdes occurring in many plants, characterized by their property of producing a soapy lather
scurfy:	detached from the epidermis in thin dry scales
serrate:	margin having teeth directed upward toward the tip
spatulate:	broad and rounded at the apex, tapering gradually toward the base
staminate:	furnished with stamens, the pollen-bearing organs of seed plants
stipule:	an appendage at the base of a petiole
sucker:	a shoot from the roots or lower part of the stem of a plant capable of producing another plant above soil
tomentose:	having a dense, wool-like covering
winterkill:	to kill or die by exposure to winter weather

Foothills

Montane

Sub-alpine

Alpine

Plains

Southwest Mesas and Foothills

Southwest Canyons

Southwest Deserts and Parks

Tables

Woody Alpine Plants, 11,500 feet and above.
Woody Sub-Alpine Plants, 10,000-11,500 feet.
Woody Montane Plants, 8,000-10,000 feet.
Woody Foothill Plants, 6,000-8,000 feet.
Woody Plains Plants, 4,000-6,000 feet.
Woody Plants on Western Slope Mesas, 6,000-8,000 feet.
Woody Plants of the Southwest Canyons, 4,000-6,000 feet.
Woody Plants of Southwest Deserts and Parks, 4,000-6,000   feet.

The botanical names and most distinctive characteristics of the plants are *italicized*. The common names are in all CAPITAL letters.

*Abbreviations used under the column *Part of State* are "N" for North, "C" for Central, and "S" for South.

†In the column *Size,* the sizes shown are:

mat, under four inches
creeping, 4-12 inches
low, 1-3 feet
medium, 3-6 feet

tall, 6-8 feet
tree, over 8 feet, and
generally single stem

WOODY ALPINE PLANTS, 11,500 feet and above.

NAME	PART OF STATE*	ALSO FOUND IN	SUN OR SHADE	SIZE†	LEAVES	FLOWERS	FRUIT	STEMS	COMMON OR RARE	PAGE
Abies lasiocarpa ALPINE FIR	N,S,C	Sub-alpine	Sun	Dwfd. tree	Short needles, *flat*	Inconspicuous	Purple cones	Smooth bark	Common	70
Dryas octapetala MOUNTAIN DRYAD	N,S,C	—	Sun	Creeping	Small, matted	White, *8-petals*; July	Feathery; Aug.	Spreading	Rare	97
Juniperus communis LOW JUNIPER	N,S,C	Sub-alpine, montane, foothills, mesas	Sun & shade	Low	*Short needles, striped*	Inconspicuous	Blue berries	Evergreen	Common	108
Paronychia pulvinata ROCKY MOUNTAIN NAILWORT	N,C	—	Sun	*Cushion*	Moss-like	Tiny, greenish; July	Inconspicuous, Sept.	Mat-like	Rare	121
Picea engelmannii ENGELMANN SPRUCE	N,S,C	Sub-alpine	Sun	Dwfd. tree	Short needles, *square*	Inconspicuous	Small, brown cones	Rough, brown bark	Common	125
Pinus aristata BRISTLECONE PINE	N,S,C	Sub-alpine	Sun	Dwfd. tree	5 needles	Inconspicuous	*Bristly* cones	Rough, dark bark	Rare	125
Pinus flexilis LIMBER PINE	N,S,C	Sub-alpine	Sun	Dwfd. tree	5 needles, *limber*	Small	Large cones	Smooth bark	Rare	126
Populus balsamifera BALSAM POPLAR	C	Sub-alpine, montane, foothills	Shade	Tree	Green above, whitish below	Catkins	Cottony	Fragrant bud	Rare	127

NAME	PART OF STATE*	ALSO FOUND IN	SUN OR SHADE	SIZE†	LEAVES	FLOWERS	FRUIT	STEMS	COMMON OR RARE	PAGE
Potentilla fruticosa BUSH CINQUEFOIL	N,S,C	Sub-alpine, montane, foothills, mesas	Shade	Low	Small 5-parted	*Yellow;* July	Dry, brown, persistent	Brown bark, shreddy	Common	128
Ribes montigenum RED-FRUITED GOOSEBERRY	N,S,C	Sub-alpine	Shade	Low	5-lobed	Purple to green	*Red berries;* Aug.	Spiny	Common	144
Ribes wolfii WOLF'S CURRANT	S,C	Sub-alpine, montane	Shade	Low	Large, lobed	Yellowish-white to red; July	Black berries; Aug.	*Smooth*	Common	144
Salix anglorum SKYLAND WILLOW	N,S,C	—	Sun	Creeping	Small, round	Catkin bloom; small heads	Cottony	Mat, *yellow*	Common	151
Salix brachycarpa BARRENGROUND WILLOW	N,S,C	Sub-alpine	Shade	Low	Small, *oblong*	Catkin bloom; small heads	Cottony	Brown to yellow	Common	151
Salix cascadensis CASCADE WILLOW	N	—	Sun	*Creeping*	Small, round	Catkin bloom; small heads	Cottony	Yellow	Rare	151
Salix nivalis SNOW WILLOW	N	—	Sun	Creeping	Small, round	Catkin bloom; small heads	Cottony	*Smallest*	Rare	151
Salix saximontana SUMMIT WILLOW	N,S,C	—	Sun	*Low, mat*	Small, round	Catkin bloom; small heads	Cottony	Mat plant	Common	151

WOODY SUB-ALPINE PLANTS, 10,000-11,500 feet (Mainly in most shady places).

NAME	PART OF STATE*	ALSO FOUND IN	SIZE†	LEAVES	FLOWERS	FRUIT	STEMS	COMMON OR RARE	PAGE
Betula glandulosa BOG BIRCH	N,C	Montane	Med.	Small, round, *leathery*	Catkins	Dry catkins	Glandular	Common	83
Chimaphila umbellata PIPSISSEWA	N,C	Montane	Very low	Small, *evergreen*	Purple, lavender	Dry pods	Woody peren.	Rare	87
Gaultheria humifusa WESTERN WINTERGREEN	N,S,C	—	Creeping	Small, evergreen	Waxy bells; June	*Red,* edible; August	Vining	Rare	103
Juniperus communis LOW JUNIPER	N,S,C	Alpine, montane, foothills, mesas	Low	Short, striped needles	Inconspicuous	Blue berries	Evergreen	Common	108
Kalmia polifolia BOG KALMIA	N,C	—	Creeping	Small, evergreen	*Tiny rose;* July	Dry	Poisonous	Rare	113
Linnaea borealis AMERICAN TWINFLOWER	N,S,C	Montane, foothills	Creeping	Tiny, round	Twin, pink bells	Inconspicuous	Fragrant	Common	116
Lonicera involucrata TWINBERRY HONEYSUCKLE	N,S,C	Foothills, mesas, montane	Med.	Large, oval	Twin, yellow; June	*Twin, black;* August	Gray	Common	116
Pachystima myrsinites MYRTLE PACHYSTIMA	N,S,C	Montane, foothills, mesas	Low	Small, *boxwood-like*	Tiny, green-purple	Tiny, dry	Evergreen	Common	121

NAME	PART OF STATE*	ALSO FOUND IN	SIZE†	LEAVES	FLOWERS	FRUIT	STEMS	COMMON OR RARE	PAGE
Phyllodoce empetriformis RED MOUNTAIN HEATH	West-N	—	Low	Ever-green	*Tiny, rose bells;* June	Small; July	In swamps	Rare	123
Populus balsamifera BALSAM POPLAR	C	Alpine, montane, foothills	Tree	Green above; whitish below	Catkins	Cottony	Green-white; fragrant buds	Rare	127
Populus tremuloides QUAKING ASPEN	N,S,C	Montane, foothills, mesas	Tree	Heart-shaped; long petioles	Catkins	Cottony	Smooth, white	Common	127
Potentilla fruticosa BUSH CINQUEFOIL	N,S,C	Alpine, montane, foothills, mesas	Low	5-parted	Yellow; *all Summer*	Brown, dry; all winter	Brown, flaky	Common	128
Rhododendron albiflorum WHITE-FLOWERED AZALEA	Routt Forest	Montane	Med.	Small *pale, twisted*	White	Dry	Peat bogs	Rare	138
Ribes montigenum RED-FRUITED GOOSEBERRY	N,S,C	Alpine	Low	5-lobed	Green-purple; July	Red berries; August	Spiny	Common	144
Ribes wolfii WOLF'S CURRANT	S,C	Alpine, montane	Low	Large, lobed	Yellow-ish; July	*Black berries;* August	Brown, smooth	Common	144

NAME	PART OF STATE*	ALSO FOUND IN	SIZE†	LEAVES	FLOWERS	FRUIT	STEMS	COMMON OR RARE	PAGE
Rubus parviflorus SALMONBERRY	West–N,S,C	Montane	Low	Very large; deeply lobed	White; July	Red berries; August	Simple	Common	148
Salix bebbiana BEBB WILLOW	East–N,S,C	Montane, foothills	Tall to tree	Ovate	Silver to yellow	Dry catkins	Smooth, spotted	Common	152
Salix brachycarpa BARRENGROUND WILLOW	N,S,C	Alpine	Low	Small, oblong	Catkin bloom	Cottony	Brown-yellow	Common	151
Salix caudata WHIPLASH WILLOW	N,S,C	Montane, foothills	Tall	Glandular, margined	Silver to yellow	Pods with "cotton balls"	*Thick, reddish*	Common	154
Salix monticola MOUNTAIN WILLOW	N,S,C	Montane	Med. to tall	Light green to yellowish	Fuzzy pussies	Cottony	Red-brown & yellow	Very Common	152
Salix pseudolapponum SUBALPINE WILLOW	S	—	Low to med.	Small, narrow	Fuzzy pussies	Dry catkins	Shiny brown-gray	Rare	151
Salix subcoerulea BLUE WILLOW	N,S,C	Montane	Med. to tall	Narrow, oblong	Pussies	Dry catkins	*Blue bloom*	Common	155
Salix wolfii WOLF'S WILLOW	N,S,C	Montane	Med.	Small, narrow	Pussies	Dry catkins	Brown, yellow	*Rare*	152

NAME	PART OF STATE*	ALSO FOUND IN	SIZE†	LEAVES	FLOWERS	FRUIT	STEMS	COMMON OR RARE	PAGE
Sambucus pubens RED-BERRIED ELDER	N,S,C	Montane	Med.	Compound	White cluster	*Red berries;* August	Brown	Common	158
Shepherdia canadensis RUSSET BUFFALOBERRY	N,S,C	Montane, foothills	Med.	Gray-green, frosty	Small, yellow; June	Red berries; July	Brown, scurfy	Common	161
Sorbus scopulina WESTERN MOUNTAIN ASH	N,S,C	Montane	Med. to tree	Compound	Small, white heads	*Orange berries*	Brown	Rare	162
Vaccinium caespitosum DWARF BILBERRY	N,C	Montane	Low	Small, oval	Small, waxy; June	Small, blue; August	*Round*	Common	168
Vaccinium myrtillus MYRTLE BLUEBERRY	N,S,C	Montane	Low	Very small	Small, waxy; June	*Small, blue-black;* August	Angled	Common	168
Vaccinium scoparium BROOM HUCKLEBERRY	N,C	Montane	Low	Very small	Small, waxy; June	Small, *red*	Angled	Common	168
Viburnum pauciflorum MOOSEBERRY VIBURNUM	N,C	Montane	Low to med.	Medium, lobed	Small, white; June	Red berries; July	Smooth	*Very Rare*	169

WOODY SUB-ALPINE PLANTS, 10,000-11,500 feet (Generally in sunny places).

NAME	PART OF STATE*	ALSO FOUND IN	SIZE†	LEAVES	FLOWERS	FRUIT	STEMS	COMMON OR RARE	PAGE
Abies lasiocarpa ALPINE FIR	S,C	Alpine	Dwf'd. tree	Evergreen needles; flat	Small	*Upright cones; purple*	Smooth bark	Common	70
Juniperus communis LOW JUNIPER	N,S,C	Alpine, montane, foothills, mesas	Low	Evergreen needles; striped	Small, inconspicuous	Blue berries	Evergreen	Common	108
Picea engelmannii ENGELMANN SPRUCE	N,S,C	Alpine	Dwf'd. tree	Sharp, square needles	Small, pink	Small, brown cones	Brown bark	Common	125
Pinus aristata BRISTLECONE PINE	N,S,C	Alpine	Small tree	Evergreen, 5 in bunch	Small	Bristly cones	*Pitch on needles*	Rare	125
Pinus flexilis LIMBER PINE	N,S,C	Alpine	Small tree	Evergreen 5 in bunch	Small	Large cones	Limber needles	Rare	126
Ribes coloradense COLORADO CURRANT	S,C	—	Low	Large, 5-lobed	*Pinkish*, small	Black berries	Sticky	Common	143
Rubus strigosus WILD RED RASPBERRY	N,S,C	Montane, foothills	Low	Compound	Small, white; June	Red berries; edible; August	Thorny	Common	148
Spiraea densiflora SUBALPINE SPIREA	N	—	Low	Small	Small, *rose*	Dry	Brown	Rare	163

NAME	PART OF STATE*	ALSO FOUND IN	SIZE†	LEAVES	FLOWERS	FRUIT	STEMS	COMMON OR RARE	PAGE
WOODY MONTANE PLANTS, 8,000-10,000 feet (Generally in moist or shady places)									
Abies concolor WHITE FIR	West-S; C	Foothills	Tree	Large, flat needles	Incon-spicuous	*Upright*, purple cones	Smooth, gray	Common	70
Acer glabrum ROCKY MOUNTAIN MAPLE	N,S,C	Foothills, mesas	Tall to tree	3-lobed, red stems	Greenish; May	*Twin winged*	Gray, smooth	Common	70
Alnus tenuifolia THINLEAF ALDER	N,S,C	Foothills, mesas	Tall to tree	Large, ribbed	*Pink catkins*	Tiny "cones"; Nov.	Smooth gray bark	Common	72
Betula glandulosa BOG BIRCH	N,C	Sub-Alpine	Med	Small, round, *leathery*	Catkins	dry catkins	Gland-ular, red	Common	83
Betula fontinalis WATER BIRCH	N,S,C	Foothills, canyons	Tall to tree	Dark green	Catkins; May	Tiny "cones"	*Red-brown cherry-like*	Common	83
Chimaphila umbellata PIPSISSEWA	N,C	Sub-alpine	Creep-ing very low	Small, *Ever-green*	Purple, lavender	Dry pods	Woody, peren.	Rare	87
Clematis pseudoalpina ROCKY MOUNTAIN CLEMATIS	S,C	Foothills	Frail vine	Compound	Delicate, lavender	Dry, fuzzy	Frail vine, climbing	Rare	91

NAME	PAGE	COMMON OR RARE	STEMS	FRUIT	FLOWERS	LEAVES	SIZE†	ALSO FOUND IN	PART OF STATE*
Cornus stolonifera RED OSIER DOGWOOD	93	Common	*Red stems*	White berries	White heads; June	Large, oval	Med.	Plains, canyons, foothills, mesas	N,S,C
Juniperus communis LOW JUNIPER	108	Common	Ever-green	Blue berries	Incon-spicuous	*3-striped needles*	Low	Alpine, sub-alpine, foothills, mesas	N,S,C
Linnaea borealis AMERICAN TWINFLOWER	116	Common	Fra-grant	Incon-spicuous	*Twin, pink bells*	Tiny, round	Creep-ing	Sub-alpine, foothills	N,S,C
Lonicera involucrata TWINBERRY HONEYSUCKLE	116	Common	Gray	*Twin black;* August	Twin yellow; June	Large, oval	Med.	Sub-alpine, foothills, mesas	N,S,C
Menziesia ferruginea RUSTY MENZIESIA	119	Rare	Brown	Dry	Greenish-purple	*Rusty-brown*	Med.	—	West-N
Pachystima myrsinites MYRTLE PACHYSTIMA	121	Common	Ever-green	Dry	Tiny, green-purple July	*Boxwood-like*	Low	Sub-alpine, foothills mesas	N,S,C
Physocarpus monogynus MOUNTAIN NINEBARK	124	Common	Brown, shreddy	Red-brown dry July	*Small, white heads*	Small, lobed	Low	Foothills	N,S,C
Picea pungens BLUE SPRUCE	125	Common	Rough, brown	Large, brown cones	Incon-spicuous	*Square, sharp needles*	Tree	Foothills	S,C

NAME	PART OF STATE*	ALSO FOUND IN	SIZE†	LEAVES	FLOWERS	FRUIT	STEMS	COMMON OR RARE	PAGE
Populus angustifolia NARROWLEAF COTTONWOOD	N,S,C	Foothills, mesas, canyons	Tall tree	Large, narrow Willow-like	Catkins	Cottony	Rough, whitish	Common	127
Populus balsamifera BALSAM POPLAR	C	Alpine, sub-alpine foothills	Tall tree	Green-above; whitish-below	Catkins	Cottony	Green-white, fragrant bud	Rare	127
Populus tremuloides QUAKING ASPEN	N,S,C	Sub-alpine, foothills	Tree	Heart shaped, long petioles	Catkins	Cottony	*Smooth*, white	Common	127
Prunus pennsylvanica PIN CHERRY	N,S,C	Foothills	Tall	Cherry-like	*White*, flat heads	*Red berries*	Cherry-like	Rare	130
Prunus virginiana WESTERN CHOKECHERRY	N,S,C	Sub-alpine Mesas, plains canyons, foothills	Tall	Oval	White, pendant cluster	*Black berries* when ripe	Spotted	Common	131
Pseudotsuga taxifolia DOUGLAS FIR	N,S,C	Foothills	Tree	*Flat, soft* needles	Inconspicuous	*Dark brown cones*	Rough, brown	Common	132
Rhododendron albiflorum WHITE-FLOWERED AZALEA	Routt Forest	Sub-alpine	Med.	*Twisted, pale*	Small, white,	Dry	Peat bogs	Rare	138

NAME	PART OF STATE*	ALSO FOUND IN	SIZE†	LEAVES	FLOWERS	FRUIT	STEMS	COMMON OR RARE	PAGE
Ribes inerme WHITESTEM GOOSEBERRY	N,S,C	Foothills	Low	Lobed	Green-ish or pinkish bells; June	*Black berries*	Thorny to spineless	Common	143
Ribes setosum REDSHOOT GOOSEBERRY	S,C	Foothills	Low	Lobed	Small, white; June	*Purple berries*	Thorny	Common	144
Ribes wolfii WOLF'S CURRANT	S,C	Alpine, sub-alpine	low	*Large, lobed*	Yellow-ish; July	Black berries; Aug.	Smooth	Common	144
Rosa, sp. WILD ROSE	N,S,C,	Foothills, plains, mesas, canyons	Low	Compound	Pink & white	Red "apples"	Thorny, red	Common	145
Rubus parviflorus SALMONBERRY	West-N,S,C	Sub-alpine	Low	*Very large, deeply lobed*	White; June	Red berries; August	Simple	Common	148
Salix bebbiana BEBB WILLOW	East-N,S,C	Foothills sub-alpine	Tall to tree	Ovate	Silver to yellow	Dry catkins	*Smooth* spotted	Common	152
Salix caudata WHIPLASH WILLOW	N,S,C	Sub-alpine, foothills	Tall	Glandular margins	Silver to yellow	Dry catkins	*Thick, reddish*	Common	154

NAME	PART OF STATE*	ALSO FOUND IN	SIZE†	LEAVES	FLOWERS	FRUIT	STEMS	COMMON OR RARE	PAGE
Salix monticola MOUNTAIN WILLOW	C	Sub-alpine	Med. to tall	Upper-green; under-pale	Fuzzy pussies	Dry catkins	Red brown & yellow	Very common	152
Salix scouleriana SCOULER WILLOW	N,S,C	Foothills	Tall to tree	Large	Pussies	Cottony	Gray; yellow twigs	Common	152
Salix subcoerulea BLUE WILLOW	N,S,C	Sub-alpine	Med. to tall	Lanceolate	Pussies	Cottony	*Blue bloom*	Common	155
Salix wolfii WOLF'S WILLOW	N,S,C	Sub-alpine	Med.	Small, narrow	Pussies	Cottony	*Brown, yellow*	*Rare*	152
Sambucus melanocarpa BLACKBEAD ELDER	West-C	—	Med.	Compound	White, round heads	Blue-black berries	*Brown, pithy*	Rare	158
Sambucus pubens RED-BERRIED ELDER	N,S,C	Sub-alpine	Med.	Compound	White cluster	*Red berries;* August	Brown	Common	158
Shepherdia canadensis RUSSET BUFFALOBERRY	N,S,C	Sub-alpine, foothills	Med.	*Gray-brown, frosty*	Small, yellow; June	Red; July	Brown, scurfy	Common	161
Sorbus scopulina WESTERN MOUNTAIN ASH	N,S,C	Sub-alpine	Med. to tree	Compound	Small, white heads	*Orange;* Sept.	Brown	Rare	162

NAME	PART OF STATE*	ALSO FOUND IN	SIZE†	LEAVES	FLOWERS	FRUIT	STEMS	COMMON OR RARE	PAGE
Symphoricarpos oreophylos MOUNTAIN SNOWBERRY	N,S,C	Foothills	Low	Small, round	Small, pink bells	*White berries*	Runners	Common	164
Vaccinium caespitosum DWARF BILBERRY	N,C	Sub-alpine	Low	Small, oval	Small, white to red waxy; June	Small, blue; Aug.	*Round*	Common	168
Vaccinium myrtillus MYRTLE BLUEBERRY	N,S,C	Sub-alpine	Low	Very small	Small, waxy; June	*Small, blue-black Aug.*	Angled	Common	168
Vaccinium scoparium BROOM HUCKLEBERRY	N,C	Sub-alpine	Low	Very small	Small, waxy; June	*Small red*	Angled	Common	168
Viburnum pauciflorum MOOSEBERRY VIBURNUM	N,C	Sub-alpine	Low to med.	Med. lobed	Small, white	Red berries	Smooth	*Very Rare*	169

NAME	PART OF STATE*	ALSO FOUND IN	SIZE†	LEAVES	FLOWERS	FRUIT	STEMS	COMMON OR RARE	PAGE
					WOODY FOOTHILL PLANTS, 6,000-8,000 feet—Eastern Slope (Mainly on north slopes or part shade.)				
Amelanchier sp. SERVICE-BERRY	N,S,C	Mesas	Tall	Small, round	Small, white; May-June	*Blue, edible*	*Bronzy*	Common	73
Clematis ligusticifolia WESTERN VIRGIN'S BOWER	N,S,C	Mesas, canyons, plains	Vine	Compound, twining	*White stars*	White, feathery	Vigorous vine	Common	91
Clematis pseudoalpina ROCKY MOUNTAIN CLEMATIS	S,C	Montane	Vine, frail	Compound	*Delicate, lavender*	Dry, fuzzy	Frail vine, climbing	Rare	91
Corylus cornuta BEAKED FILBERT	East-N,C	—	Tall	Heavy, veined	Catkins; April	*Nuts in husk*	Light, brown	Rare	94
Crataegus chrysocarpa FIREBERRY HAWTHORN	N,C	—	Tall to tree	Thick, round	White heads	*Yellow to orange, dry*	Thorny	Rare	95
Crataegus succulenta FLESHY HAWTHORN	N,C	Canyons	Tall to tree	Dark green	White heads	*Red, edible*	Thorny	Common	96
Elaeagnus angustifolia RUSSIAN OLIVE	N,S,C	Canyons, plains	Tall to tree	*Gray, narrow*	Yellow, fragrant	Gray "olives"	Green to brown	Rare	98

NAME	PART OF STATE*	ALSO FOUND IN	SIZE†	LEAVES	FLOWERS	FRUIT	STEMS	COMMON OR RARE	PAGE
Elaeagnus commutata SILVERBERRY	C	—	Med.	Small, silvery	Small, yellow	Silvery berries	Silvery	Rare	98
Juniperus communis LOW JUNIPER	N,S,C	Alpine, sub-alpine, montane, mesas	Low	3-striped needles	Small	Blue berries	Ever-green	Common	108
Linnaea borealis AMERICAN TWINFLOWER	N,S,C	Sub-alpine, montane	Creep-ing	Tiny, round	*Twin-bells*	Small, dry	Fragrant	Common	116
Lonicera involucrata TWINBERRY HONEYSUCKLE	N,S,C	Sub-alpine, montane, mesas	Med.	Large, oval	Twin-yellow; June	*Twin, black;* Aug.	Gray	Common	116
Pachystima myrsinites MYRTLE PACHYSTIMA	N,S,C	Sub-alpine montane, mesas	Low	Ever-green, boxwood-like	Small	Small	Ever-green	Common	121
Parthenocissus vitacea WOODBINE	N,S,C	Mesas	Vine	Large, *5-parted*	Small	Blue berries	No aerial rootlets	Rare	122
Physocarpos bracteatus TWINPOD NINEBARK	West-C	—	Med.	Small, lobed	Small, white; May	Dry, brown; July	Brown	Rare	123
Physocarpos monogynus MOUNTAIN NINEBARK	N,S,C	Montane	Low	Small, lobed	*Small, white;* May	Dry red-**Brown;** July	Brown, shreddy	Common	124

NAME	PART OF STATE*	ALSO FOUND IN	SIZE†	LEAVES	FLOWERS	FRUIT	STEMS	COMMON OR RARE	PAGE
Pinus contorta LODGEPOLE PINE	N,S,C	Montane	Tree	2 in bundle	Inconspicuous	Twisted cones	Dark	Common	125
Populus balsamifera BALSAM POPULAR	C	Alpine, sub-alpine, montane	Tall tree	Green above whitish below	Catkins	Cottony	Fragrant bud	Rare	127
Populus tremuloides QUAKING ASPEN	N,S,C	Sub-alpine montane	Tree	Long petioles	Catkins	Cottony	*White bark*	Common	127
Potentilla fruticosa BUSH CINQUEFOIL	N,S,C	Sub-alpine, montane, mesas	Low	5-parted	Yellow; all Summer	Brown; all Winter	Brown, flaky	Common	128
Prunus pennsylvanica PIN CHERRY	N,S,C	Montane	Tall	Cherry-like	White, flat heads	*Red berries*	Cherry-like	Rare	130
Prunus virginiana WESTERN CHOKECHERRY	N,S,C	Plains, sub-alpine, montane, mesas, canyons	Tall	Oval	White, pendant clustered	*Black berries*	Spotted	Common	131
Pseudotsuga taxifolia DOUGLAS FIR	N,S,C	Montane	Tree	Flat, soft, evergreen	Inconspicuous	*Brown cones*	Rough, brown	Common	132

NAME	PART OF STATE*	ALSO FOUND IN	SIZE†	LEAVES	FLOWERS	FRUIT	STEMS	COMMON OR RARE	PAGE
Rhus radicans WESTERN POISON IVY	N,S,C	Canyons	Low to med.	3-parted	Inconspicuous	White berries	Brown	Rare	139
Ribes aureum GOLDEN CURRANT	N,S,C	Plains, mesas	Med.	3-lobed	*Yellow tubes;* May	Yellow, black; July	Brown	Common	142
Sambucus canadensis AMERICAN ELDER	N,C	—	Med. to tall	Compound	White heads; June	Black berries; Aug.	Brown, pithy	Rare	158
Shepherdia canadensis RUSSET BUFFALOBERRY	N,S,C	Sub-alpine, montane	Med.	*Gray-brown,* frosty	Small, yellow; June	*Red berries;* July	Brown, scurfy	Common	161
Symphoricarpos occidentalis WESTERN SNOWBERRY	N,S,C	Plains	Low	Small	Small, pink	*Off-white berries*	Erect, brown	Common	165
Symphoricarpos orbiculatis CORALBERRY	West-N	—	Low	Small, round	Small, pink	*Red berries*	Slim runners	Rare	166
Symphoricarpos oreophilos MOUNTAIN SNOWBERRY	N,S,C	Montane	Low	Small, round	Small, pink buds; June	*White berries*	Runners	Common	164

WOODY FOOTHILLS PLANTS, 6,000-8,000 feet—Mainly along streams on Eastern Slope

NAME	PART OF STATE*	ALSO FOUND IN	SIZE†	LEAVES	FLOWERS	FRUIT	STEMS	COMMON OR RARE	PAGE
Acer glabrum ROCKY MOUNTAIN MAPLE	N,S,C	Mesas, montane	Tall to tree	3-lobed, red-stemmed	Small, green; May	*Twin-winged;* July	Gray, smooth	Common	170
Acer negundo BOX ELDER	N,S,C	Canyons, plains, mesas	Tree	*Compound;* 3-7 leaflets	Small, pink tassels	*Twin-winged*	Rough gray to grn.	Common	72
Alnus tenuifolia THINLEAF ALDER	N,S,C	Montane, mesas	Tall to tree	Large, ribbed	*Pink catkins;* April	*Tiny "cones"*	Smooth gray	Common	72
Amorpha fruticosa FALSE INDIGO	East-C	Plains	Med. to tall	Compound	*Spikes of Indigo;* Aug.	Small pods Sept.	Gray	Rare	75
Betula fontinalis WATER BIRCH	N,S,C	Montane, canyons	Tall to tree	Dark green	Catkins; May	Tiny "cones"; Fall	Brown, *cherry-like*	Common	83
Celtis occidentalis WESTERN HACKBERRY	S,C	Plains, mesas, canyons	Low to tall tree	Elm-like, lop-sided	Incon-spicuous	Dark berries	*Gray, corky*	Rare	85
Clematis ligusticifolia WESTERN VIRGIN'S BOWER	N,S,C	Canyons, mesas	Vine	Compound	*White stars*	White, feathery	Gray vine	Common	91

NAME	PART OF STATE*	ALSO FOUND IN	SIZE†	LEAVES	FLOWERS	FRUIT	STEMS	COMMON OR RARE	PAGE
Cornus stolonifera RED OSIER DOGWOOD	N,S,C	Plains, montane, canyons, mesas	Med.	Large, oval	White heads	White berries	*Bright red*	Common	93
Corylus cornuta FILBERT	East– N,C,	—	Med.	Heavy-veined	Catkins; April	*Nuts in husk*	Light brown	Rare	94
Pachystima myrsinites MYRTLE PACHYSTIMA	N,S,C	Sub-alpine montane, mesas	Low	*Boxwood-like*	Green-purple small	Tiny, dry	Ever-green	Common	121
Picea pungens BLUE SPRUCE	C,S	Montane	Tree	Sharp, square	Incon-spicuous	*Large brown cones*	Rough, brown	Common	125
Populus acuminata LANCE-LEAF POPLAR	N	—	Tree	*Lance-shaped*	Catkins	Cottony	Smooth, green-white	Rare	126
Populus angustifolia NARROWLEAF COTTONWOOD	N,S,C	Montane, mesas, canyons	Tall tree	*Large, narrow*	Catkins	Cottony	Rough, whitish	Common	127
Populus tremuloides QUAKING ASPEN	N,S,C	Mesas, montane sub-alpine	Tree	Long petioles	Catkins	Cottony	*Smooth, white*	Common	127
Potentilla fruticosa BUSH CINQUEFOIL	N,S,C	Alpine, sub-alpine, montane, mesas	Low	5-parted	Yellow; all Summer	Dry brown; all Winter	Brown, flaky	Common	128

NAME	PART OF STATE*	ALSO FOUND IN	SIZE†	LEAVES	FLOWERS	FRUIT	STEMS	COMMON OR RARE	PAGE
Prunus americana AMERICAN PLUM	East-N,S,C	Plains	Tall to tree	Simple	White; May	*Red plums;* July	Gray	Common	129
Prunus virginiana WESTERN CHOKECHERRY	N,S,C	Sub-alpine, canyons, plains, montane, mesas	Tall	Large, oval	White clusters; May	*Black berries;* July	Spotted	Common	131
Ptelea baldwinii HOPTREE	East-S	Arkansas River, canyons	Tall	3-parted	Greenish	*Hop-like,* winged	Smooth, fragrant	Rare	132
Ribes americanum AMERICAN BLACK CURRANT	C	—	Low to med.	3- to 5-lobed	Greenish	*Black berries*	Smooth	Rare	142
Ribes inerme WHITESTEM GOOSEBERRY	N,S,C	Montane	Low	Lobed	Greenish-pinkish bells; June	*Black berries;* Aug.	Thorny to spineless	Common	143
Ribes setosum REDSHOOT GOOSEBERRY	S,C	Montane	Low	Lobed	Small, white	*Purple berries*	Thorny	Common	144
Rosa sp. WILD ROSE	N,S,C	Montane, plains, mesas, canyons	Low	Compound	Pink & white; June	*Red "apples"*	Thorny, red	Common	145
Salix amygdaloides PEACH LEAF WILLOW	N,S,C	Plains	Tree	Narrow	Pussies	Dry	Dark, ridged	Common	154

NAME	PART OF STATE*	ALSO FOUND IN	SIZE†	LEAVES	FLOWERS	FRUIT	STEMS	COMMON OR RARE	PAGE
Salix bebbiana BEBB WILLOW	East-N,S,C	Sub-alpine, montane	Tall to tree	Ovate	Silver to yellow	Dry catkins	*Smooth*, spotted	Common	152
Salix caudata WHIPLASH WILLOW	N,S,C	Sub-alpine, montane	Tall	Glandular margins	Silver to yellow	Dry catkins	*Thick, reddish*	Common	154
Salix exigua SANDBAR WILLOW	N,S,C	Mesas, plains, desert, canyons	Tall to tree	Very narrow	Pussies	Catkins	*Slim, red-brown*	Common	154
Salix irrorata BLUESTEM WILLOW	N,S,C	—	Tall	Narrow	Pussies	Catkins	*Blue bloom*	Common	155
Salix scouleriana SCOULER WILLOW	N,S,C	Montane	Tall	Large, narrow	Pussies	Cottony catkins	Gray; yellow twigs	Common	152
Symphoricarpos occidentalis WESTERN SNOWBERRY	N,S,C	Plains	Low	Small, round	Pink-white	Dirty-white	Erect, matted	Common	165
Viburnum lentago NANNYBERRY VIBURNUM	East-N	Plains	Tall	Large, oval	*White heads*	Blue-black berries; edible	Brown-gray	Rare	169
Vitis vulpina WILD GRAPE	E	—	Vine	Large, lobed	Incon-spicuous	*Black grapes*	Brown	Rare	169

WOODY FOOTHILLS PLANTS, at Elevations of 6,000-8,000 feet—Eastern Slope (Mainly in dry, sunny places—south slopes.)

NAME	PART OF STATE*	ALSO FOUND IN	SIZE†	LEAVES	FLOWERS	FRUIT	STEMS	COMMON OR RARE	PAGE
Amorpha nana LOW FALSE INDIGO	C	—	Low	Compound, green	*Spikes of indigo;* Aug.	Small pods; Sept.	Gray	Rare	75
Amelanchier sp. SERVICE-BERRY	N,S,C	Mesas	Tall	Small, round	Small, white	*Blue berries;* edible	Bronzy	Common	73
Arctostaphylos uva-ursi KINNIKINNICK	N,S,C	Mesas, montane	Creeping	Small, evergreen	Tiny, waxy; June	*Red berries*	Evergreen	Common	76
Aster sp. ASTER	N,S,C	Plains	Low	Small, various	White, pink, purple	Dry heads	Part-woody, peren.	Common	79
Berberis repens CREEPING MAHONIA	N,S,C	Montane	Creeping	*Holly-like*	Yellow	Blue-black berries	Evergreen	Common	82
Ceanothus fendleri FENDLER CEANOTHUS	S,C	—	Low	Small, part-evergreen	White heads; June	Inconspicuous	*Greenish*	Common	84
Ceanothus ovatus INLAND CEANOTHUS	N,C	—	Med.	Small, green	*White heads*	Dry; Fall	Gray	Rare	84

NAME	PART OF STATE*	ALSO FOUND IN	SIZE†	LEAVES	FLOWERS	FRUIT	STEMS	COMMON OR RARE	PAGE
Ceanothus velutinus SNOWBRUSH CEANOTHUS	N,C	Montane	Med.	*Thick, aromatic*	Small, white; June	Dry	Ever-green	Common	85
Cercocarpus montanus TRUE MOUNTAIN MAHOGANY	N,S,C	Montane, canyons	Med.	Wedge-shaped	Small, red; May	Twisted, feathery	Gray	Common	87
Chrysothamnus nauseosus GREENPLUME RABBIT BRUSH	N,S,C	Plains, canyons, desert, mesas	Med.	Small, narrow	*Yellow heads;* Sept.	Dry, white	Green-ish	Common	90
Clematis orientalis ORIENTAL CLEMATIS	C	—	Vine	Deeply cut	Yellow	Fuzzy or shiny	Vine	Common	91
Crataegus sp. COLORADO HAWTHORN	N,S,C	Montane, mesas	Tall or tree	Large, toothed	White; May	*Red or black*	Bronzy	Common	95
Eriogonum sp. WILD BUCKWHEAT	N,S,C	Plains, mesas, canyons, desert	Low	Small, various	Tiny in heads	Dry, brown	Gray, part-woody	Common	98
Fallugia paradoxa APACHE PLUME	S,C	Canyons	Med.	Small, divided	*White;* 5-petalled	Silvery-purple plumes	Gray	Common	100
Haplopappus sp. GOLDENWEED	N,S,C	Plains, canyons, mesas	Low	Small	Small, *yellow*	Dry	Part-woody	Common	104

NAME	PART OF STATE*	ALSO FOUND IN	SIZE†	LEAVES	FLOWERS	FRUIT	STEMS	COMMON OR RARE	PAGE
Helianthemum bicknellii FROSTWEED	C	—	Low	Small	*Yellow;* 5-petalled	Dry	Part-woody, peren.	Common	105
Holodiscus dumosus BUSH ROCK SPIREA	N,S,C	Mesas, canyons	Med.	Small, wedge-shaped, toothed	*White plumes;* June	Dry heads	Brown	Common	105
Jamesia americana CLIFF JAMESIA	C	Montane	Med.	Thick-ish, gray	*Waxy, ivory;* May	Dry brown	Brown, striated	Common	106
Juniperus communis LOW JUNIPER	N,S,C	Alpine, sub-alpine, montane, mesas	Low	Ever-green, *striped*	Small	Blue berries	Ever-green	Common	108
Juniperus scopulorum COLORADO JUNIPER	N,S,C	Mesas	Tall to tree	*ever-green* needles	Small	Blue-gray berries with "bloom"	Brown	Common	110
Loranthaceae family MISTLETOE	N,S,C	Montane, canyons, mesas	Small	Small, pale	Small, pink, inconspicuous	White to red or orange berries	*Parasitic;* pale, woody	Rare	117
Mamillaria sp. PINCUSHION CACTUS	S,C	Plains	Low	None	Green to purple	Green to scarlet	Fleshy; small *"nipples"*	Rare	119

NAME	PART OF STATE*	ALSO FOUND IN	SIZE†	LEAVES	FLOWERS	FRUIT	STEMS	COMMON OR RARE	PAGE
Opuntia arborescens CANE CACTUS	S,C	Plains, desert	Med. to tall	None	Large, red-purple	Yellow, hairy	*Green,* fleshy	Common	120
Pinus edulis PIÑON PINE	N,S,C	Mesas, canyons	Tall to tree	Ever-green, 2 in bunch	Small	*Small* cones;	Gray, rough	Common	126
Pinus ponderosa PONDEROSA PINE	N,S,C	Montane, plains, canyons	Large tree	Long needles, 2-3 in bunch	Small	Large cones	Brown, rough	Common	126
Prunus besseyi WESTERN SAND CHERRY	East-N	Plains	Low	Simple	White: May	*Blue-black* plums	Brown	Rare	129
Prunus virginiana WESTERN CHOKECHERRY	N,S,C	Plains, mesas, montane	Tall	Large, oval	White clusters	*Black* clusters	Spotted	Common	131
Purshia tridentata ANTELOPE BRUSH	N,S,C	Montane, mesas, canyons	Low	3-parted	Yellow, fragrant	Dry pods	Gray	Common	132
Quercus sp. OAK	S,C	Canyons, mesas, desert	Tall to tree	Lobed	Tiny, yellow tassels	Acorns; July	Gray, rough	Common	133

NAME	PART OF STATE*	ALSO FOUND IN	SIZE†	LEAVES	FLOWERS	FRUIT	STEMS	COMMON OR RARE	PAGE
Rhus glabra SMOOTH SUMAC	N,S,C	Canyons	Low to med.	Compound	Inconspicuous	*Red berries, heads;* Sept.	Brown, smooth	Common	138
Rhus trilobata SKUNKBRUSH SUMAC	N,S,C	Mesas, plains, canyons, desert	Med. to tall	3-parted	Tiny, yellow clusters, very early	Red clusters; July	Gray, fragrant	Common	140
Ribes cereum WAX CURRANT	N,S,C	Montane	Med.	Small, round	Pink tubes; June	*Red berries*	Cherry-like	Common	142
Robinia neomexicana NEW MEXICAN LOCUST	S	Canyons	Tall to tree	Compound	*Pink "Peas";* June	Brown, hairy, pea-pods	Thorny	Rare	145
Rubus deliciosus THIMBLEBERRY	N,S,C	Montane	Med.	Lobed	*Large, white;* June	Purple berries	Brown, flaky	Common	148
Rubus strigosus WILD RED RASPBERRY	N,S,C	Sub-alpine, montane	Low	Compound	Small, white; June	*Red berries;* Aug.	Prickly	Common	148
Yucca glauca SMALL SOAPWEED	N,S,C	Plains	Low	Long, narrow, evergreen	White "lilies;" July	Dry pods; Oct.	Evergreen	Common	171

WOODY PLAINS PLANTS, 4,000-6,000 feet—on Eastern Slope (Mostly in damp or partly shaded spots.)

NAME	PART OF STATE*	ALSO FOUND IN	SIZE†	LEAVES	FLOWERS	FRUIT	STEMS	COMMON OR RARE	PAGE
Acer negundo BOX ELDER	N,S,C	Foothills, canyons, mesas	Tree	Compound, 3-7 leaflets	Small, pink tassels	*Twin-winged*	Rough gray	Common	72
Amorpha fruticosa FALSE INDIGO	East-C	Foothills	Tall	Small, compound	*Indigo, in spikes;* July	Dry spikes	Gray	Rare	75
Baccharis salicina WILLOW BACCHARIS	West-C, Baca Co	Mesas	Tall	Willow-like	Greenish heads	*Cottony heads*	Gray	Common	80
Celtis occidentalis WESTERN HACKBERRY	S,C	Mesas, foothills, canyons	Low to tall tree	*Elm-like, lop-sided*	Inconspicuous	Dark berries	Gray, corky	Rare	85
Cornus stolonifera RED OSIER DOGWOOD	N,S,C	Foothills, canyons, mesas, montane	Med.	Large, oval	White in heads	White berries	*Bright red*	Common	93
Elaeagnus angustifolia RUSSIAN OLIVE	N,S,C	Foothills, canyons	Shrubby tree	*Narrow, gray*	Small, yellow, fragrant	Gray "olives"	Green to brown	Rare	98

NAME	PART OF STATE*	ALSO FOUND IN	SIZE†	LEAVES	FLOWERS	FRUIT	STEMS	COMMON OR RARE	PAGE
Populus sargentii PLAINS COTTONWOOD	N,S,C	Foothills, canyons	Large tree	Large, broad	Catkins	*Cotton*	Rough bark	Common	127
Prunus americana AMERICAN PLUM	N,S,C	Foothills	Tall to tree	Simple	White	*Red plums*	Gray	Common	129
Prunus virginiana WESTERN CHOKECHERRY	N,S,C	Sub-alpine, mesas, montane, foothills, canyons	Tall	Oval	White pendant clusters	*Black berries*, when ripe	Spotted	Common	131
Ribes aureum GOLDEN CURRANT	N,S,C	Foothills, mesas	Med.	3-lobed	*Yellow tubes*	Black or yellow berries	Brown	Common	142
Salix amygdaloides PEACHLEAF WILLOW	East-N,S,C	Foothills	Tree	Peach-like	Catkins	Cottony	*Ridged, black bark*	Common	154
Salix exigua COYOTE WILLOW	N,S,C	Foothills, canyons, mesas, deserts	Tall	Very narrow	Catkins	Cottony	Light red-brown	Common	154
Sapindus drummondii WESTERN SOAPBERRY	East-S	—	Shrubby tree	Compound	Tiny, white	*Poisonous*, amber berries; Sept.	red-brown, scaly	Rare	159

NAME	PART OF STATE*	ALSO FOUND IN	SIZE†	LEAVES	FLOWERS	FRUIT	STEMS	COMMON OR RARE	PAGE
Symphoricarpos occidentalis WESTERN SNOWBERRY	N,S,C	Foothills	Low	Small	Small, pink; June	Off-white berries	Erect, matted	Common	165
Tamarix gallica TAMARISK	East & West-S	Canyons	Tall	Juniper-like, light green	*White & pink plumes;* Summer	Tiny, dry	Red-dish to black	Common	166
Viburnum lentago NANNYBERRY VIBURNUM	East-N	Foothills	Tall	Large, oval	White heads	*Edible blue-black berries*	Brown-gray	Rare	169

NAME	PART OF STATE*	ALSO FOUND IN	SIZE†	LEAVES	FLOWERS	FRUIT	STEMS	COMMON OR RARE	PAGE
Amorpha canescens LEADPLANT	East	—	Low	*Gray, compound*	Spikes of indigo	Dry spikes	Brown-gray	Rare	75
Artemisia sp. SAGEBRUSH	N,S,C	Mesas, desert	Med.	*Small, gray*	Tiny, yellow	Dry plumes	Gray	Common	77
Aster sp. ASTER	N,S,C	Foothills	Low	Small, various	*White, pink, purple*	Dry heads	Part-woody, peren.	Common	79
Atriplex sp. SALTBRUSHES	West-S	Desert, mesas	Tall	Small, gray	Small	*Winged*	Gray	Common	80
Chrysothamnus sp. RABBIT BRUSH	N,S,C	Mesas, foothills, desert, canyons	Low to tall	Narrow	*Yellow heads*	Whitish heads	Green-ish	Common	90
Desmanthus illinoensis BUNDLE FLOWER	East-S	—	Low	Pinnate	*Pea-like, whitish*	Dry	Part-woody, peren.	Rare	97
Ditaxis humilis Spurge family	East	—	Low	Small	Small	Dry	Pur-plish sap, *erect*	Rare	97

WOODY PLAINS PLANTS, 4,000-6,000 feet—on Eastern Slope (Mainly in dry, sunny locations.)

NAME	PART OF STATE*	ALSO FOUND IN	SIZE†	LEAVES	FLOWERS	FRUIT	STEMS	COMMON OR RARE	PAGE
Eriogonum sp. WILD BUCKWHEAT	East	Canyons, mesas, foothills, desert	Low	Small	*Tiny,* numerous	Dry	Part-woody, peren.	Common	98
Eurotia lanata COMMON WINTERFAT	East, West-S	Canyons, mesas	Med.	Thread-like, com-pound	Small, pink plumes	Wooly plumes	White, wooly	Rare	100
Frankenia jamesii PEARLY MOCKHEATHER	West-S, East-S	Canyons	Low	*Linear*	White	Dry capsule	Erect, part-woody	Rare	103
Gutierrezia sp. SNAKEWEED	N,S,C	Canyons, desert, mesas	Low	Small	Small, *yellow*	Dry	Crowded, part-woody	Very common	104
Haploesthes greggii Composite family	East-S	—	Low	*Linear, fleshy*	Yellow, com-posite	Dry	Part-woody	Rare	104
Haplopappus sp. GOLDENWEED	N,S,C	Foothills, mesas, canyons	Low	Small	*Yellow,* ray-flowers	Dry	Part-woody	Common	104
Mamillaria sp. PINCUSHION CACTUS	S,C	Foothills, mesas	Low	None	Green to purple	Green to scarlet	Fleshy "nipples"	Rare	119

NAME	PART OF STATE*	ALSO FOUND IN	SIZE†	LEAVES	FLOWERS	FRUIT	STEMS	COMMON OR RARE	PAGE
Menodora scabra ROUGH MENODORA	East-C	—	Low	Small, narrow	Small, yellow, funnel-like	*Twin pods*	Woody at base	Rare	119
Mimosa borealis CAT'S CLAW	East-S, Baca Co.	—	Med.	Delicate, compound	Long, pink exserted stamens	Dry seed pods	Prickly	Rare	120
Opuntia arborescens CANE CACTUS	S,C	Desert, foothills	Med.	None	Pink; May	*Yellow*, hairy	*Fleshy*, edges comb-like	Common	120
Opuntia davisii LOW CANE CACTUS	S	Mesas	Low	None	Yellow	Yellow	Fleshy, spreading	Rare	121
Pinus ponderosa PONDEROSA PINE	N,S,C	Foothills, montane	Tree	2-3 in bundle	Inconspicuous	Large cones	Brown-gray	Common	126
Prunus besseyi WESTERN SANDCHERRY	East-N	Foothills	Low	Medium	White; May	*Edible plums*, blue-black	Brown, spreading	Rare	129
Prunus virginiana WESTERN CHOKECHERRY	N,S,C	Montane, mesas, foothills, canyons	Tall	Oval	White clusters	Black berries	Spotted	Common	131

NAME	PART OF STATE*	ALSO FOUND IN	SIZE†	LEAVES	FLOWERS	FRUIT	STEMS	COMMON OR RARE	PAGE
Rhus trilobata SKUNKBUSH SUMAC	N,S,C	Canyons, mesas, foothills, montane	Med.	*3-parted, aromatic*	Tiny yellow clusters; April	Clusters of red berries	Aromatic, brown	Common	140
Rosa sp. WILD ROSE	N,S,C	Canyons, foothills, montane, mesas	Low	Compound	Pink & white; June	*Red hips*	*thorny*, red	Common	145
Senecio sp. OLDMAN	N,S,C	Mesas	Low	*Grasslike*	Yellow, ragged	Dry heads	Part-woody, peren.	Common	160
Yucca glauca SMALL SOAPWEED	N,S,C	Foothills	Low	Long, narrow, evergreen	*White lilies on stem*	Large, dry pods	Evergreen	Common	171

WOODY PLANTS ON WESTERN SLOPE MESAS & FOOTHILLS—6,000-8,000 feet (Mainly on north slopes or moist places.)

NAME	PART OF STATE*	ALSO FOUND IN	SIZE†	LEAVES	FLOWERS	FRUIT	STEMS	COMMON OR RARE	PAGE
Acer glabrum ROCKY MOUNTAIN MAPLE	N,S,C	Montane, foothills	Tall to tree	3-lobed, red stems	Small, green; May	Twin-winged	Smooth, gray	Common	70
Acer grandidentatum BIGTOOTH MAPLE	West-S	—	Tall	Lobed, bigtoothed	Small; May	Twin-winged	Smooth, gray	Rare	71
Acer negundo BOXELDER	N,S,C	Plains, foothills, canyons	Tree	Compound, 3-7 leaflets	Small, pink tassels	*Twin-winged*	Dark, rough	Common	72
Alnus tenuifolia THINLEAF ALDER	N,S,C	Foothills, montane	Tall to tree	Large, ribbed	*Pink catkins*	Tiny "cones"	Smooth, gray	Common	72
Baccharis sp. GROUNDSEL TREE	West & East-S	Plains	Tall	Small; willow-like	Greenish tassels	*Whitish "cotton balls"*	Green	Rare	80
Celtis occidentalis WESTERN HACKBERRY	S,C	Plains, foothills, canyons	Tree	*Elm-like, lop-sided*	Inconspicuous	Dark berries	Gray, corky	Rare	85
Clematis ligusticifolia WESTERN VIRGIN'S BOWER	N,S,C	Foothills, canyons, plains	Vine	Compound, clasping	*White stars;* May	Feathery, white	Vigorous vining	Common	91

NAME	PART OF STATE*	ALSO FOUND IN	SIZE†	LEAVES	FLOWERS	FRUIT	STEMS	COMMON OR RARE	PAGE
Cornus stolonifera RED OSIER DOGWOOD	N,S,C	Foothills, plains, montane, canyons	Med.	Large, oval	Small, white heads	White berries	*Bright red*	Common	93
Crataegus erythropoda SHINY-LEAVED HAWTHORN	West-N	—	Tree	Shiny diamond-shaped	White, in heads	Dark berries	Red spines; brown	Common	95
Crataegus rivularis RIVER HAWTHORN	West-N	—	Tall to tree	ovate, toothed	White heads	Dark red "apples"	Black, curved spines; bronzy	Rare	96
Crataegus saligna WILLOW HAWTHORN	C & Gunnison River	—	Tall	*Willow-like*	White heads	Black "apples"	Slender black spines; bronzy	Rare	96
Lonicera involucrata TWINBERRY HONEYSUCKLE	N,S,C	Sub-alpine, mesas, montane	Med.	Large, oval	Twin, yellow	*Black, twin*	Gray	Common	116
Pachystima myrsinites MYRTLE PACHYSTIMA	N,S,C	Sub-alpine, montane, foothills	Low	*Small, ever-green*	Tiny	Tiny	Ever-green	Common	121
Parthenocissus vitacea WOODBINE	N,S,C	foothills	Vine	Large, 5-parted	Small	Blue berries	No aerial rootlets	Rare	122
Physocarpus pubescens DWARF HAIRY NINEBARK	West-S	Canyons	Low	Small, round	*Small, white*	Dry, brown	Shreddy brown bark	Rare	124

NAME	PART OF STATE*	ALSO FOUND IN	SIZE†	LEAVES	FLOWERS	FRUIT	STEMS	COMMON OR RARE	PAGE
Populus angustifolia NARROW LEAF COTTONWOOD	N,S,C	Montane, foothills, canyons	Tall tree	*Long, narrow,* willow-like	Catkins	Cottony	Rough, whit-ish	Common	127
Populus tremuloloides QUAKING ASPEN	N,S,C	Foothills, montane, sub-alpine	Tree	Long, petioles	Catkins	Cottony	*Smooth, white*	Common	127
Potentilla fruticosa BUSH CINQUEFOIL	N,S,C*	Alpine, sub-alpine, montane	Low	Small, 5-parted	*Yellow; all Summer*	Dry, brown; all Winter	Brown, flaky	Common	128
Prunus virginiana WESTERN CHOKECHERRY	N,S,C	Sub-alpine, foothills, plains, montane, canyons	Tall	Large, oval	White pendant	*Black berries,* when ripe	Spotted	Common	131
Rhamnus betulaefolia BIRCHLEAF BUCKTHORN	West-S	–	Med.	*Large, veined*	Green-ish	Black berries	Brown	Rare	137
Rhamnus smithii SMITH BUCKTHORN	S,C	–	Tall	Willow-like	Green-ish, small	*Black berries*	Brown-black	Rare	137
Ribes aureum GOLDEN CURRANT	N,S,C	Foothills, plains	Med.	3-lobed	*Golden tubes*	Black or yellow berries	Dark	Common	142

NAME	PART OF STATE*	ALSO FOUND IN	SIZE†	LEAVES	FLOWERS	FRUIT	STEMS	COMMON OR RARE	PAGE
Ribes leptanthum TRUMPET GOOSEBERRY	N,S,C	Canyons	Low to med.	Small, lobed	White-yellow bells	Black berries	*Old-smooth; new-thorny*	Rare	144
Rosa sp. WILD ROSE	N,S,C	Foothills, montane, plains canyons	Low	Compound	Pink & white	*Red hips*	Thorny, red	Common	145
Salix exigua COYOTE WILLOW	N,S,C	Foothills, plains desert, canyons	Tall to tree	*Very narrow*	Catkins	Cottony	Light red-brown	Common	154
Sambucus ELDER	West-C	—	Tall	Compound	White in heads	*Black berries, flat heads*	Brown, pithy	Rare	158
Shepherdia argentea SILVER BUFFALOBERRY	S,C	Canyons	Tall	Gray, narrow	Small, yellow; early	*Bright red berries*	Gray, thorny	Common	161
Spiraea caespitosa TUFTED ROCKMAT	West-N	—	Mat	Very small, matted	Tiny, white, on stems	Fuzzy, dry heads	*Matted, pendant*	Rare	163
Spiraea lucida SHINYLEAF SPIREA	West-N	—	Low	Small, birch-like	White heads	Dry heads	Erect	Rare	163
Symphoricarpos sp. SNOWBERRY	West-N	Foothills, montane	Med.	Small	Small, pink; June	White berries; Sept.	Runners	Common	164

WOODY PLANTS ON WESTERN SLOPE MESAS AND FOOTHILLS—6,000-8,000 feet (Mainly in hot, dry areas.)								
NAME	PART OF STATE*	ALSO FOUND IN	SIZE†	LEAVES	FLOWERS	FRUIT	STEMS	COMMON OR RARE	PAGE
Amelanchier sp. SERVICE-BERRY	N,S,C	Foothills	Tall	Small, round	White; May-June	*Blue berries;* July	Bronzy	Common	73
Arctostaphylos patula GREENLEAF MANZANITA	West-S,C	Canyons	Med.	Leathery, ever-green	Tiny, waxy; June	Small, white to brown berries	*Pol-ished; red, brown*	Rare	77
Arctostaphylos uva-ursi KINNIKINNICK	N,S,C	Foothills, montane	Creep-ing	Small, ever-green	Tiny, waxy; June	*Red; berries*	Ever-green	Common	76
Artemisia spinescens BUD SAGEBRUSH	West-S	—	Low	Finely dis-sected	Yellow heads	Covered with dry heads	Gray, spiny	Rare	79
Artemisia tridentata BIG SAGEBRUSH	West-N,S,C	Plains, desert	Med to tall	*3-parted,* gray	Small heads	Gray heads	Gray	Common	77
Atriplex sp. SALTBRUSHES	West-S	Desert, plains	Low to med.	Small, gray	Small	*Winged*	Gray	Common	80
Berberis fendleri COLORADO BARBERRY	S,C	Canyons	Low	Small	Small, yellow	*Red berries;* Aug.	Spiny	Common	81

NAME	PART OF STATE*	ALSO FOUND IN	SIZE†	LEAVES	FLOWERS	FRUIT	STEMS	COMMON OR RARE	PAGE
Brickellia sp. BRICKELLBUSH	West-S,C	Canyons	Low	*Triangular*	Off-white	Dry	Part-woody, peren.	Common	83
Cercocarpus ledifolius CURL-LEAF MOUNTAIN MAHOGANY	West-N,S,C	Canyons	Tall	*Narrow, leathery*	Red tubes; July	Feathery	Brown	Common	86
Chrysothamnus sp. RABBIT BRUSH	N,S,C	Foothills, canyons, desert	Tall	Small, narrow	Yellow heads	White heads	Greenish	Common	90
Cowania mexicana CLIFFROSE	West-S	Canyons	Med.	Small, divided	Pale-yellow; May	Dry with tails	Dark	Common	94
Echinocactus sp. BARREL CACTUS	N,S,C	Canyons, desert	Low	None	Yellow to purple, at top	*Not spiny* greenish	Very fleshy	Rare	97
Echinocereus sp. HEDGEHOG CACTUS	N,S,C	Canyons, desert,	Low	None	Yellow to purple, on sides	Spiny greenish or red, dry	Very fleshy	Rare	98
Ephedra sp. MORMON TEA	West-S,C	Desert, canyons	Med.	None	Small, yellow	Small, in husk	Evergreen, *round*	Common	99

NAME	PART OF STATE*	ALSO FOUND IN	SIZE†	LEAVES	FLOWERS	FRUIT	STEMS	COMMON OR RARE	PAGE
Eriogonum sp. WILD BUCKWHEAT	N,S,C	Foothills, plains, desert, canyons	Low	Small	Tiny, pink & white	Small, dry	Part-woody, peren.	Common	98
Eurotia lanata COMMON WINTERFAT	S,C	Plains, canyons	Low to med.	Thread-like	Small, tufted	Seed plumes w/silky hairs	*Gray, wooly*	Rare	100
Fendlera rupicola FALSE MOCKORANGE	S,C	Canyons	Tall	Small	*White & pink-ish*	Dry pods, 4-parted	Gray, straight	Common	101
Fendlerella utahensis LITTLE FENDLERBUSH	West-N	—	Low to med.	Small	*Small, white*	Dry	Crowd-ed, shreddy	Rare	101
Grayia brandegei SPINELESS HOP-SAGE	S	Canyons, desert	Low	Fleshy-mealy	Incon-spicuous	Winged scales	Mealy	Rare	104
Grayia spinosa SPINY HOP-SAGE	S	Canyons, desert	Low	Fleshy-mealy	Incon-spicuous	Winged scales	*Thorny*	Rare	104
Gutierrezia lucida SNAKEWEED	N,S,C	Desert, canyons, plains	Low	Small	Small, *yellow*	Dry	Crowd-ed, part-woody	Very common	104

NAME	PART OF STATE*	ALSO FOUND IN	SIZE†	LEAVES	FLOWERS	FRUIT	STEMS	COMMON OR RARE	PAGE
Haplopappas sp. GOLDENWEED	N,S,C	Plains, canyons, foothills	Low	*Glandular*	Yellow	Dry	Part-woody	Common	104
Holodiscus dumosus BUSH ROCK SPIREA	N,S,C	Canyons, foothills	Med.	Small wedges, fragrant, toothed	White heads	Dry heads	Brown	Common	105
Juniperus communis LOW JUNIPER	N,S,C	Alpine, sub-alpine, montane	Low	*3-striped needles*	Small	Blue berries	Ever-green	Common	108
Juniperus monosperma CHERRYSTONE JUNIPER	S,C	Canyons	Tall to tree	Ever-green needles	Small	Copper to blueish berries	Brown	Common	108
Juniperus scopulorum COLORADO JUNIPER	N,S,C	Foothills	Tall to tree	Whip-cord needles	Small	*Blue-gray berries*	Ever-green	Common	110
Juniperus utahensis UTAH JUNIPER	West-S	Canyons	Tall to tree	*Ever-green, Juniper-like*	White, Phlox-like	Fibrous; red-brown to blue-gray	Woody	Common	111
Leptodactylon pungens FALSE JUNIPER	West-S	Canyons	Low	Ever-green juniper-like	White, phlox-like; Spring	Small, dry	Woody	Common	113

NAME	PART OF STATE*	ALSO FOUND IN	SIZE†	LEAVES	FLOWERS	FRUIT	STEMS	COMMON OR RARE	PAGE
Loranthaceae family MISTLETOE	N,S,C	Montane, canyons, foothills	Small	Small, pale	Small, pink, inconspicuous	White, red or orange berries	Pale, woody, parasitic	Rare	117
Lycium pallidum DESERT-THORN	West-S	Desert, canyons	Low to med.	Small, narrow	Greenish-purple bells	Orange-red berries	Dark, angled, thorny	Common near ruins	118
Mamillaria sp. PINCUSHION CACTUS	S,C	Plains, foothills	Low	None	Green to purple	Green to scarlet	Fleshy stems	Rare	119
Opuntia sp. PRICKLY PEAR CACTUS	N,S,C	Plains, desert, canyons	Low	None	Pink & yellow	Red & yellow	Thorny, fleshy	Common	120
Peraphyllum ramosissimum SQUAW APPLE	S,C	Canyons	Med.	Narrow, leathery	Pink; May	*Red apples*	Dark, smooth	Common	122
Philadelphus microphyllus LITTLELEAF MOCKORANGE	S,C	Canyons	Med.	Small, narrow	*White;* May	Dry pods, 4-parted	Much branched, straight	Rare	123
Pinus edulis PIÑON PINE	S,C	Foothills	Shrub-by tree	Twin needles	Small	*Small cones*	Dark brown	Common	126

NAME	PART OF STATE*	ALSO FOUND IN	SIZE†	LEAVES	FLOWERS	FRUIT	STEMS	COMMON OR RARE	PAGE
Purshia tridentata ANTELOPE BRUSH	N,S,C	Foothills, montane, canyons	Low	3-parted	*White fragrant*	Dry pods	Brown	Common	132
Quercus sp. OAK	S,C	Desert, foothills, canyons	Tall to trees	Lobed	Small, yellow tassels	*Acorns*	Rough, brown	Common	133
Quercus undulata DESERT OAK	S,C	Desert	Low	*Small, crisped*	Yellow tassels	Tiny acorns	Brown	Rare	136
Rhus trilobata SKUNKBRUSH SUMAC	N,S,C	Desert, mesas, foothills, canyons	Med.	3-parted, aromatic	Small, yellow	*Red acid,* glandular	Brown, aromatic	Common	140
Rosa sp. WILD ROSE	N,S,C	Canyons, montane, foothills, plains	Low	Compound	Pink	*Red hips*	Thorny	Common	145
Salix lasiandra PACIFIC WILLOW	West-S	Canyons	Tree	Very narrow	Small catkins	Dry	Tree-like; dark, rough	Rare	154
Sarcobatus vermiculatus BLACK GREASEWOOD	East & West-S	Desert	Low to tall	*Fleshy, salty*	Inconspicuous	Discs, green to pink or red	Gray-thorny	Common	159
Senecio sp. OLDMAN	N,S,C	Plains	Low	Small	*Yellow heads*	Dry	Part-woody	Common	160

NAME	PART OF STATE*	ALSO FOUND IN	SIZE†	LEAVES	FLOWERS	FRUIT	STEMS	COMMON OR RARE	PAGE
Shepherdia rotundifolia SILVERLEAF BUFFALOBERRY	West-S	—	Med.	*Silvery, mealy*	Tiny, yellow	Mealy-gray berries	Gray, mealy	Common	162
Stanleya pinnata PRINCE'S PLUME	West-S	Mesas, desert	Low	Pinnate or simple	Long, yellow plumes	Dry pods	Part-woody	Common	163
Tetradymia sp. HORSEBRUSH	West-S	Desert, canyons	Low	*Spine-like, wooly*	Small, yellow tubes	Dry	Smooth or thorny	Rare	167
Yucca baccata INDIAN BANANA	West-S	Canyons desert	Low	Broad, stiff	White "lilies," short stem	Fleshy cucumbers	Ever-green	Common	171
Yucca harrimaniae STUBBY-LEAF SOAPWEED	West-S	—	Low	Broad, reflexed	White "lilies"	Dry seed pods	Ever-green	Common	172
Yucca neomexicana SHORT-LEAF YUCCA	West-S	Canyons, desert	Low	*Short, narrow*	White "lilies" on stem	Dry seed pods	Ever-green	Rare	173

NAME	PART OF STATE*	ALSO FOUND IN	SIZE†	LEAVES	FLOWERS	FRUIT	STEMS	COMMON OR RARE	PAGE
Acer grandidentatum BIGTOOTH MAPLE	West-S	Mesas	Tall to tree	Large, toothed	Small, green	*Twin-winged*	Gray, smooth	Common	71
Acer negundo BOXELDER	N,S,C	Plains, mesas, foothills	Tree	*Compound, 3-7 leaflets*	Pink catkins	Twin-winged	Green to black	Common	72
Arctostaphylos patula GREENLEAF MANZANITA	S,C	Mesas	Low to med.	Leathery, evergreen	Tiny, waxy	Dark berries	*Polished bronze*	Rare	77
Berberis fendleri COLORADO BARBERRY	S,C	Mesas	Low	Small	Small, yellow	*Red berries; Aug.*	Spiny	Common	81
Berberis fremontii FREMONT MAHONIA	West-S	—	Med. tall	*Holly-like, evergreen*	Yellow clusters	Blue berries; Aug.	Gray	Rare	81
Berberis haematocarpa RED HOLLY-GRAPE	West-S	—	Tall	Evergreen, shiny, narrow	Small, yellow clusters	*Red berries; edible*	Dark	Rare	81
Betula fontinalis WATER BIRCH	N,S,C	Montane, foothills	Tall	Dark green	Catkins; May	Tiny "cones;" Fall	Brown *cherry-like*	Common	83

NAME	PART OF STATE*	ALSO FOUND IN	SIZE†	LEAVES	FLOWERS	FRUIT	STEMS	COMMON OR RARE	PAGE
Brickellia sp. BRICKELLBUSH	S,C	Mesas	Low	*Triangular*	Off-white	Dry pods	Part-woody, peren.	Common	83
Celtis occidentalis WESTERN HACKBERRY	S,C	Mesas, plains foothills	Tree to shrub	*Elm-like, lop-sided*	Inconspicuous	Dark berries	Gray, corky	Rare	85
Cercis occidentalis WESTERN REDBUD	West-S	—	Tall to tree	*Heart-shaped*	Purple-pink; early	Dry "pea-pods"	Dark smooth	Rare	85
Cercocarpus ledifolius CURL-LEAF MOUNTAIN MAHOGANY	West N,S,C	Mesas	Tall	*Narrow, leathery*	Tiny; May	Feathery	Brown	Common	86
Cercocarpus montanus TRUE MOUNTAIN MAHOGANY	N,S,C	Montane, foothills	Med.	Wedge-shaped	Small, red; early	*Feathery plumes*	Gray	Common	87
Chamaebatiaria millefolium FERNBUSH	West-S	—	Med.	*Compound, ferny*	White heads	Dry heads	Gray	Rare	87
Chrysothamnus nauseosus RABBIT BRUSH	N,S,C	Plains, desert, mesas	Tall	Small, linear	*Yellow heads*	Whitish heads	Greenish	Common	90
Clematis ligusticifolia WESTERN VIRGIN'S BOWER	N,S,C	Foothills, mesas	Vine	Compound tendrils	White stars	*Fuzzy white*	Vines	Common	91

NAME	PART OF STATE*	ALSO FOUND IN	SIZE†	LEAVES	FLOWERS	FRUIT	STEMS	COMMON OR RARE	PAGE
Coleogyne ramosissima BLACKBRUSH	West-S	Desert	Low	Tiny, narrow	*Yellow;* May	Small capsules	Dark	Common	93
Cornus stolonifera RED OSIER DOGWOOD	N,S,C	Plains, foothills, mesas, montane	Med.	Large, oval	White heads	White berries	*Bright red*	Common	93
Cowania mexicana CLIFFROSE	West-S	Mesas	Med.	Small, divided	*Pale-yellow;* May	Dry with tails	Dark	Common	94
Crataegus sp. HAWTHORN	N,S,C	Foothills, mesas	Tall to tree	Large, oval	White heads	*Red to black berries*	Bronzy to dark	Common	95
Echinocactus sp. BARREL CACTUS	N,S,C	Desert, canyons	Low	None	At top, yellow to purple	Not Spiny, greenish or red, dry	Fleshy balls	Rare	97
Echinocereus sp. HEDGEHOG CACTUS	N,S,C	Desert, canyons	Low	None	On sides, yellow to purple	*Spiny,* greenish or red, dry	Fleshy	Rare	98
Elaeagnus angustifolia RUSSIAN OLIVE	N,S,C	Foothills, plains	Tall to tree	*Narrow, gray*	Tiny, yellow; fragrant	Gray berries	Green to black	Rare	98
Ephedra sp. MORMON TEA	West-S	Desert, mesas	Low to med.	None	Small, yellow	Nuts in tiny husk	*Green, round*	Common	99

NAME	PART OF STATE*	ALSO FOUND IN	SIZE†	LEAVES	FLOWERS	FRUIT	STEMS	COMMON OR RARE	PAGE
Eriogonum sp. WILD BUCKWHEAT	N,S,C	Foothills, desert, mesas, plains, canyons	Low	Small	Tiny heads	Dry heads	Part-woody, peren.	Common	98
Eurotia lanata COMMON WINTERFAT	S,C	Plains, mesas	Low to med.	Thread-like	Small	Dry	*White, wooly*	Rare	100
Fallugia paradoxa APACHE PLUME	S,C	Foothills	Med.	Small, divided	*White; 5-petalled*	Silvery-purple plumes	Gray	Common	100
Fendlera rupicola FALSE MOCKORANGE	West-S,C	Mesas	Tall	Small, narrow	*White, 4 petals*	Dry, 4-parted	Erect, gray	Rare	101
Forestiera neomexicana MOUNTAIN PRIVET	S,C	—	Med. to tall	Privet-like	Small, yellow	*Small, black berries, whitish "bloom"*	Gray, smooth	Rare	102
Forsellesia meionandra GREASEBUSH	West-S	Desert	Low	*Very tiny; numerous*	Solitary	Dry	Green-ish, spiny	Rare	102
Frankenia jamesii PEARLY MOCKHEATHER	S	Plains	Low	Small, narrow	Small, white	Dry capsules	*Erect, crowded*	Rare	103
Fraxinus anomala SINGLELEAF ASH	West-S	—	Tall to tree	Simple	Small, green-ish	*"Canoe paddles"*	Ash gray, opposite	Common	103

NAME	PART OF STATE*	ALSO FOUND IN	SIZE†	LEAVES	FLOWERS	FRUIT	STEMS	COMMON OR RARE	PAGE
Grayia sp. HOP-SAGE	West-S	Mesas, desert	Low	*Fleshy, mealy*	Inconspicuous	Winged scales	Thorny or mealy	Rare	104
Gutierrezia sp. SNAKEWEED	N,S,C	Plains, mesas, desert	Low	Small	*Small, yellow*	Small, dry	Erect, crowded	Very common	104
Haplopappus sp. GOLDENWEED	N,S,C	Foothills, mesas, plains	Low	Small	*Yellow*	Dry	Part-woody, peren.	Common	104
Holodiscus dumosus BUSH ROCK SPIREA	N,S,C	Foothills, mesas	Med.	Small, fragrant	White heads	Dry heads	Brown	Common	105
Juniperus monosperma CHERRYSTONE JUNIPER	S,C	Mesas	Tall to tree	Whipcord needles	Small	*Gray berries*	Evergreen	Common	108
Juniperus utahensis UTAH JUNIPER	West-S	Mesas	Tall to tree	Whipcord needles	Small	*Large, gray berries*	Evergreen	Common	111
Larrea tridentata CREOSOTE BUSH	S	Desert	Tall	*Tiny, evergreen; fragrant*	Tiny, yellow	Small nuts in fuzzy white balls	Greenish	Rare	113
Leptodactylon pungens FALSE JUNIPER	West-S	Mesas	Very low	Evergreen, juniper-like	Phlox-like, white	Dry	Woody	Common	113

NAME	PART OF STATE*	ALSO FOUND IN	SIZE†	LEAVES	FLOWERS	FRUIT	STEMS	COMMON OR RARE	PAGE
Loranthaceae family MISTLETOE	N,S,C	Foothills, montane, mesas	Small	Small, pale	Small, pink, inconspicuous	White, red or orange berries	Pale, woody, parasitic	Rare	117
Lycium pallidum DESERT-THORN	West-S	Desert, mesas	Tall	Small, narrow	Greenish bells	*Red berries;* edible	Dark, angled	Common near ruins	118
Opuntia sp. PRICKLY PEAR	N,S,C	Desert, mesas, plains	Low	None	*Yellow & pink*	Pink & yellow	Fleshy, flat or round	Common	120
Oxytenia acerosa COPPERWEED	S	—	Med.	Small	*Yellow*	Whitish	Part-woody, peren.	Rare	121
Parryella filifolia DUNEBROOM	West-S	Desert	Low	Compound	Yellow-green	One-seed	*Rush-like*	Rare	122
Peraphyllum ramosissimum SQUAW APPLE	S,C	Mesas	Med.	Narrow, leathery	Pink; May	*Red apples*	Dark, smooth	Common	122
Philadelphus microphyllus LITTLELEAF MOCKORANGE	S,C	Mesas	Tall	Small, narrow	*White;* May	Dry pods	Straight, gray	Rare	123
Physocarpus pubescens DWARF HAIRY NINEBARK	West-S	Mesas	Low	Small, round	*Small, white heads*	Dry, brown	Brown	Rare	124
Pinus edulis PIÑON PINE	S,C	Foothills, mesas	Tall to tree	Short, twin needles	Small	*Small cones*	Evergreen	Common	126

NAME	PART OF STATE*	ALSO FOUND IN	SIZE†	LEAVES	FLOWERS	FRUIT	STEMS	COMMON OR RARE	PAGE
Pinus ponderosa PONDEROSA PINE	N,S,C	Foothills, montane	Tree	2-3 needles	Inconspicuous	Large cone	Dark	Common	126
Poliomintha incana ROSEMARY MINT	West-S	Desert	Low	Linear, aromatic	Blue to purple clusters	Smooth nutlets	Felt-like covering	Rare	126
Populus angustifolia NARROWLEAF COTTONWOOD	N,S,C	Montane, foothills, mesas	Tall tree	Large, narrow, willow-like	Catkins	Cottony	Rough, whitish	Common	127
Populus sargentii PLAINS COTTONWOOD	N,S,C	Plains, mesas, foothills	Large tree	Large, broad	Catkins	Cottony	Gray, ridged	Common	127
Prosopis glandulosa HONEY MESQUITE	S	Desert	Tall to tree	Compound	Small, creamy	"Beans" in pods	Yellowish spines, angled	Rare	128
Prunus virginiana WESTERN CHOKECHERRY	N,S,C	Sub-alpine, plains, mesas, montane, foothills	Tall	Oval	White pendant	Black berries, when ripe	Dark, spotted	Common	131
Ptelea baldwinii HOPTREE	S	Foothills	Tall	3-parted, aromatic	Small, greenish	Round "hops"	Smooth, dark	Rare	132

NAME	PART OF STATE*	ALSO FOUND IN	SIZE†	LEAVES	FLOWERS	FRUIT	STEMS	COMMON OR RARE	PAGE
Purshia tridentata ANTELOPE BRUSH	S,C	Montane, mesas, foothills	Low to med.	Small, 3-parted	*Yellow,* fragrant	Dry pods	Dark	Common	132
Quercus gambelii GAMBEL OAK	S,C	Foothills, mesas	Med. to tree	Smooth, lobed	Yellow tassels	Acorns	Gray, rough	Common	133
Quercus turbinella CALIFORNIA SCRUB OAK	West-S	—	Med.	*Holly-like, ever-green*	Yellow tassels	Small acorns	Dark	Rare	136
Quercus undulata DESERT OAK	West-S	Desert, mesas	Low to med.	*Tiny, lobed*	Yellow tassels	Tiny acorns	Tiny, gray	Rare	136
Rhus glabra SMOOTH SUMAC	N,S,C	Foothills	Low	Compound	Incon-spicuous	Red berries in heads	Smooth, brown	Common	138
Rhus radicans WESTERN POISON IVY	N,S,C	Foothills	Low to med.	*3-parted*	Incon-spicuous	White berries	Brown	Rare	139
Rhus trilobata SKUNKBRUSH SUMAC	N,S,C	Foothills. desert, mesas, plains	Med.	3-parted, aromatic	Yellow; early	Red, acid berries	Dark, aro-matic	Common	140

NAME	PART OF STATE*	ALSO FOUND IN	SIZE†	LEAVES	FLOWERS	FRUIT	STEMS	COMMON OR RARE	PAGE
Ribes leptanthum TRUMPET GOOSEBERRY	N,S,C	Mesas	Tall to med.	Lobed	Small, yellow	*Gland-ular,* red	Thorny	Rare	144
Robinia neomexicana NEW MEXICAN LOCUST	S	Foothills	Tall to tree	Com-pound	*Pink heads*	Dry, "pea pods"	Thorny	Rare	145
Rosa sp. WILD ROSE	N,S,C	Mesas, plains, montane, foothills	Low to med.	Com-pound	Pink & white	*Red hips*	Thorny	Common	145
Salix exigua SANDBAR WILLOW	N,S,C	Plains, mesas, foothills, montane	Tall to tree	Very narrow	Pussies	Cottony	Slim, red-brown	Common	154
Salix lasiandra PACIFIC WILLOW	West-S	—	Tree	Peach-like	Catkins	Dry	Dark, ridged	Rare	154
Sambucus coerulea neomex. NEW MEXICAN BLUEBERRY ELDER	S	—	Tall to tree	Com-pound	White heads	*Black heads*	Pithy, smooth	Rare	158
Shepherdia argentea SILVER BUFFALOBERRY	S,C	Mesas	Tall	Gray, narrow	Yellow, small; early	*Bright-red berries*	Gray, thorny	Common	161
Stanleya pinnata PRINCE'S PLUME	West-S	Mesas, desert	Low	Pinnate or simple	Long, yellow plumes	Dry pods	Part-woody	Common	163

NAME	PART OF STATE*	ALSO FOUND IN	SIZE†	LEAVES	FLOWERS	FRUIT	STEMS	COMMON OR RARE	PAGE
Suaeda fruticosa SEEPWEED	S	Desert	Low	*Linear, fleshy*	Small	Dry	Part-woody, rust-color	Rare	164
Tamarix gallica TAMARISK	West-S	Desert, plains	Tall	Juniper-like	*Pink & white plumes*	Small, dry	Red-young, black-old	Common	166
Tetradymia sp. HORSEBRUSH	West-S	Desert, mesas	Low	*Spine-like, wooly*	Small, yellow	Dry	Smooth or thorny	Rare	167
Thamnosma texana TEXAS DESERT RUE	S	Desert	Low	Small, narrow	Small, solitary, yellow-purple	Small, twin, yellow-green	*Aromatic*	Rare	167
Yucca angustissima FINELEAF YUCCA	West-S	—	Med.	Long, narrow	White "lilies," long stems	Dry pods	Evergreen	Rare	172
Yucca baccata INDIAN BANANA	West-S	Mesas	Low	Broad "swords"	White "lilies," short stem	*Fleshy "cucumbers"*	Evergreen	Common	171
Yucca neomexicana SHORT-LEAF YUCCA	West-S	Desert, mesas	Low	*Short, narrow*	White "lilies" on stem	Dry pods	Evergreen	Rare	173

NAME	PART OF STATE*	ALSO FOUND IN	SIZE†	LEAVES	FLOWERS	FRUIT	STEMS	COMMON OR RARE	PAGE
WOODY PLANTS OF SOUTHWEST DESERTS & PARKS—4,000-6,000 feet (Usually level and open areas.)									
Artemisia tridentata BIG SAGEBRUSH	N,S,C	Plains, mesas	Tall	*3-parted*, *gray*	Tiny, yellow	Whitish plumes	Gray, aromatic	Common	77
Atriplex sp. SALTBRUSHES	West-S	Mesas	Low to med.	Small, gray	Tiny	*Whitish, winged*	Gray	Common	80
Chrysothamnus nauseosus RABBIT BRUSH	N,S,C	Mesas, plains, canyons	Tall	Small	*Yellow heads*	Whitish heads	Green-ish, straight	Common	90
Coleogyne ramosissima BLACKBRUSH	West-S	Canyons	Low	Small	*Yellow*	Dry pods	Crowd-ed	Common	93
Echinocactus sp. BARREL CACTUS	N,S,C	Canyons, mesas	Low	None	On top, yellow to purple	Not spiny, greenish or red, dry	Fleshy balls	Rare	97
Echinocereus sp. HEDGEHOG CACTUS	N,S,C mesas	Canyons,	Low	None	On sides, yellow to purple	Spiny, greenish or red, dry	Fleshy	Rare	98
Ephedra sp. MORMON TEA	West-S	Mesas, canyons	Med.	None	Small, yellow	Husk with tiny nuts	*Slim, round, green*	Common	99

NAME	PART OF STATE*	ALSO FOUND IN	SIZE†	LEAVES	FLOWERS	FRUIT	STEMS	COMMON OR RARE	PAGE
Forsellesia meionandra GREASEBUSH	West-S	Canyons	Low	*Very tiny*	Solitary	Dry	Green-ish spiny	Rare	102
Forsellesia spinescens THORNY GREASEBUSH	West-S	Canyons	Low	*Small, oblong*	Solitary	Dry	Green-ish spiny	Rare	102
Grayia sp. HOP-SAGE	West-S	Canyons, mesas	Low	*Fleshy, mealy*	Incon-spicuous	Winged scales	Thorny or mealy	Rare	104
Gutierrezia sp. SNAKEWEED	S,C	Plains, mesas, canyons	Low	Tiny	Tiny, yellow	Tiny, dry	Many, slim, part-woody	Very common	104
Larrea tridentata CREOSOTE BUSH	S	Canyons	Med.	Small, aromatic	Tiny, yellow	Nutlets in fuzzy balls	Green-ish	Rare	113
Lycium pallidum DESERT-THORN	West-S	Canyons, mesas	Med. to tall	Narrow, pale	Green bells	Red berries	*Angled, dark*	Common near ruins	118
Opuntia arborescens CANE CACTUS	S	Plains, foothills	Tall	None	Large, pink	Yellow, spiny	*Round, spiny,* fleshy	Common	120
Opuntia davisii LOW CANE CACTUS	S	Mesas, plains	Low	None	Large, yellow	*Yellow, spiny*	Round, spiny, fleshy	Rare	121

NAME	PART OF STATE*	ALSO FOUND IN	SIZE†	LEAVES	FLOWERS	FRUIT	STEMS	COMMON OR RARE	PAGE
Parryella filifolia DUNEBROOM	West-S	Canyons	Low	Small, compound	Small, yellow-green	Small, dry, spikes; one-seeded	*Rush-like*, part-woody	Rare	122
Poliomintha incana ROSEMARY MINT	West-S	Canyons	Low	*Linear, thickish*	Blue, rose or purple	Smooth nutlets	Felt-like, hairy	Rare	126
Prosopis glandulosa HONEY MESQUITE	S	Canyons	Tall	Compound	Small, creamy	*Beans in pods*	Angled	Rare	128
Quercus undulata DESERT OAK	West-S	Canyons	Low to med.	*Holly-like, evergreen*	Yellow tassels	Small acorns	Rough, gray-black	Rare	136
Rhus trilobata SKUNKBRUSH SUMAC	N,S,C	Mesas, foothills, canyons	Med.	3-parted, aromatic	Small, yellow	Red-acid, glandular	Brown, aromatic	Common	140
Salix exigua COYOTE WILLOW	N,S,C	Plains, foothills, mesas, canyons	Tall	Very narrow	Catkins	Cottony	Light red-brown	Common	154
Sarcobatus vermiculatus BLACK GREASEWOOD	West-S	Mesas	Tall	*Small, fleshy*	Small	Small	Gray, thorny	Common	159

NAME	PART OF STATE*	ALSO FOUND IN	SIZE†	LEAVES	FLOWERS	FRUIT	STEMS	COMMON OR RARE	PAGE
Stanleya pinnata PRINCE'S PLUME	West-S	Mesas, canyons	Low	Pinnate, simple	Long yellow plumes	Dry pods	Part-woody	Common	163
Suaeda fruticosa SEEPWEED	S	Canyons	Low	*Linear*, fleshy	Small	Small	Woody base, rusty-color	Rare	164
Tamarix gallica TAMARISK	N,S,C	Canyons, plains	Tall	Cedar-like	Pink plumes; all Summer	Small, dry	New-red, old-black	Common	166
Tetradymia canescens SPINELESS GRAY HORSEBRUSH	West-S	Canyons, mesas	Low	*Small*, wooly	Small, yellow	Dry	Smooth	Rare	167
Tetradymia spinosa COTTONTHORN HORSEBRUSH	West-S	Mesas, canyons	Low	Spine-like, wooly	Small, yellow	Dry	*Thorny*	Rare	167
Thamnosma texana TEXAS DESERT RUE	West-S	Canyons	Low	*Linear, aromatic*	Small, yellow-purple	Twin-sacs, yellow-green	Broom-like	Rare	167
Yucca neomexicana SHORT-LEAF YUCCA	West-S	Canyons, mesas	Low	*Many; short, narrow*	White lilies on stem	Dry pods	Ever-green	Common	173

Abies lasiocarpa (p. 70)

Abies concolor (p. 70)

Acer negundo (p. 72)

Acer glabrum (p. 70)

Acer grandidentatum (p. 71)

Acer grandidentatum (p. 71)

Abies concolor (uniform color). WHITE FIR (see page 69)

Found at elevations of 7,500-10,000 feet in the central and southern part of the state. Sometimes in solid stands and sometimes scattered among other trees. Similar in general appearance and color to the blue spruce but of softer effect. Long, flat, blunt, silvery-blue needles and purple cones that stand upright. Makes a valuable ornamental tree.

Abies lasiocarpa (rough-fruited). ALPINE FIR (see page 69)

Growing in the subalpine zone, generally in company with the Engelmann spruce. Has smooth, white bark in contrast to the brown, flaky bark of the spruce. Short, flat needles and upright, purple cones that fall apart after frost. Not especially valuable as an ornamental.

There is a similar tree growing occasionally in the southern part of the state, *Abies lasiocarpa arizonica*, CORKBARK FIR, that has a grayish, corky bark.

Acer glabrum, in seed

Acer glabrum (smooth). ROCKY MOUNTAIN MAPLE, DWARF MAPLE (see page 69)

The Rocky Mountain maple is usually found in the montane and foothills zones or on southwestern mesas, at altitudes of 6,000-10,000 feet. It is usually found growing just above a stream, often on the north slope, or in moist places with good soil on the north slopes higher up. It is seldom found on hot, dry slopes or with its roots in the water along streams.

A tall, dense, many-stemmed shrub, it sometimes grows as tall as 10-12 feet but is usually 6-8 feet. Occasional specimens, in good soil, may become almost tree-like, with a trunk diameter of 4-6 inches.

It is readily recognized by its smooth, light-gray bark, distinctive red-stemmed maple leaf, and by the fact that it usually grows as a specimen, giving a spotty appearance to hillsides where it grows among the lower shrubs. In winter it may also be identified by the clean-looking bark and the bright-red buds. A few of the characteristic twin-winged maple seeds may usually be seen remaining on the bush in any season, which is the most positive identification.

The leaves are about as broad as long, usually 1½-2 inches wide but sometimes more, deeply three-lobed or sometimes three-parted, with long, slender petioles. The bloom in May is greenish, small, and inconspicuous, but the twin-winged seeds that follow are very attractive with their shading of color from green through yellow and red. The fall color is usually a pale yellow.

This plant is easily grown as a tall, ornamental shrub around homes, in the mountains, or in irrigated valleys.

Acer grandidentatum (big-toothed). BIGTOOTH MAPLE (see page 69)

This large shrub maple is found in many canyons throughout Utah at altitudes of 5,000-8,000 feet. It occasionally comes into Colorado from that state.

It grows on steep, well-drained hillsides or rich, moist slopes and sometimes almost down to the streams. It is usually a several-stemmed shrub, 8-12 feet tall, but sometimes becomes almost tree-like, with a diameter of 6-8 inches and height of 20 feet or more. It may be found as a single specimen or massed together.

The leaves are larger than those of the Rocky Mountain maple, do not have as deeply-cut lobes, and have round teeth. They may be 2-3 inches or more across and about as broad as high; dark-green above and lighter below.

The bloom comes early (April and May) and is rather small and inconspicuous. The fruits are typically maple, of twin-winged form, and are often quite attractive in color.

This plant is often referred to as a dwarf sugar maple, for its most outstanding characteristic is its very rich, red fall foliage. Hillsides massed or spotted with this shrub in full fall color are a sight never to be forgotten. It is strange that it has never found its way onto the lists of the nurserymen, for it makes a most attractive small tree or large shrub; probably its preference for well-drained, non-alkaline soil makes it somewhat hard to transplant.

Acer negundo (black). BOXELDER (see page 69)

A tree or a many-stemmed shrub growing in moist spots over the state in the plains, foothills, mesas and canyons at 4,000-7,500 feet. The leaves are lobed, maple-like, but compound with 3-7 leaflets. The bloom is in catkins, sometimes large and bright pink. Fruit is typically maple, twin-winged. The bark is dark and rough on old trunks and smooth and greenish with a gray "bloom" on new twigs.

This tree is often deformed by galls and it attracts boxelder bugs. It is only used as an ornamental where nothing else will grow. Its shade, where it grows in the wild, is always appreciated.

Alnus tenuifolia, staminate
and pistillate flowers

Alnus tenuifolia, bark

Alnus tenuifolia (thinleaf). ROCKY MOUNTAIN or THINLEAF ALDER

This plant grows along streams in the montane and foothills zones and on southwest mesas at altitudes of 5,000-10,000 feet, often in association with the water birch and various willows. The bark is smooth and gray, and the twigs are much less slender than those of the birch. Leaves are large and almost elm-like; buds are reddish on a short stalk.

It is usually seen as a several-stemmed shrub, 10-12 feet high, but under favorable conditions it may grow much taller and become almost tree-like with trunks 6 inches or more in diameter. It blooms in late March or early April, depending on the season and altitude. The male blooms, formed on the bush the previous fall, expand at this time until they become as large as a lady's finger, pink and white and tassel-like. They are very pretty dancing in the spring breezes. Following the expansion of the male catkins, the tiny, red female blooms and fruits begin to expand until they form seed-catkins which look much like miniature

72

ponderosa pine cones, about ¾ inches long and half that wide. These seed "cones" dry and hang on all winter, looking very attractive and furnishing a positive identification.

Outdoorsmen prefer the wood of this plant, when it is dry, for firewood. The wood is durable in water. Nitrogen-fixing bacteria form nodules on the roots of alder in much the same way as on the legumes.

This native plant is easily grown under cultivation. It makes a very attractive large shrub or may be trained to become a nice small tree.

Amelanchier, flower   Amelanchier, fruit

Amelanchier sp. SERVICE-BERRY, SHADBUSH, JUNEBERRY

Service-berries (or "sarvice-berries" as the oldtimers call them) may be found almost all over the state at elevations of 5,000-10,000 feet. They are most common in the western half of the state, growing in the mountains as tall, dense shrubs, and in rocky places and at the edge of the desert as low, dwarf shrubs. They may be found occasionally on the eastern slopes as tall, thin shrubs under trees in the foothills and mountains. The leaves are oval to round, generally about an inch long but sometimes twice that, with small teeth on the edges and prominent diagonal veins on the under side.

They have small, white flowers covering the bushes in early spring and edible, blueberry-like fruits in fall. These fruits may be about a quarter-inch in diameter, larger or smaller depending on the rainfall just previous to ripening. They have the habit of ripening one a day over a period of weeks. When this occurs

73

under favorable conditions they are very palatable, with a peculiar, bland flavor. When plentiful, they make fine preserves by canning them mixed with wild gooseberries or other acid fruit to give them flavor. The Indians dried the berries and used them as flavoring in stews and puddings or in their pemmican.

The plants may often be recognized in winter by the reddish-bronze cast to parts of their stems, as is common with other members of the apple family.

The service-berries make nice ornamental shrubs but are slow-growing and a little difficult to transplant.

Many species have been named by various botanists over the years but they are difficult to distinguish, and the best authorities now lump all found in the state under three species:

Amelanchier pumila (dwarf). SMOOTH SHAD

This name includes *A. polycarpa, pumila,* and *glabra,* of other authors. It is distinguished by having smooth buds, twigs, and leaves; grows 3-9 feet tall, with leaves usually under 2 inches long.

Amelanchier utahensis. UTAH SERVICE-BERRY

This includes *A. bakeri, crenata, eliptica, mormonica, oreophila, prunifolia* and *rubescens.* It usually has pubescence on the buds, twigs, or leaves; leaves are over 2 inches long; often grows larger and has larger fruit than the smooth species.

Amelanchier alnifolia (leaf like an alder). COMMON SHAD

This includes *A. spicata* and seems to be somewhat intermediate between the two preceding species.

Amorpha sp.,
leaf and bloom

Amorpha fruticosa
angustifolia

Amorpha canescens

74

Amorpha sp. (Greek, deformed). FALSE INDIGO

Three species are occasionally found in the state, all in the plains or foothills zones:

Amorpha fruticosa (shrubby) *angustifolia* (narrow-leaf). FALSE INDIGO

This grows to be a loose-stemmed shrub, 4-10 feet high. It is sometimes found along streams or ditches in the foothills or plains zones. It is covered with small spikes of indigo-colored, pea-like flowers in July (earlier or later depending on season and altitude). The leaves are made up of many small leaflets.

It is sometimes used in ornamental plantings, as it blooms after most shrubs are through, but it is always a rather loose, unkempt sort of shrub. Small "pea pods," attached in clusters around the seed head, may hang on most of the winter.

Amorpha nana (small) or *microphylla*. LOW FALSE INDIGO

Sometimes found on dry slopes in central Colorado at about 7,000 feet. It has leaves and bloom much like the larger shrub but seldom grows over 2 feet tall.

Amorpha canescens (hairy). LEADPLANT

This is the most valuable of all for ornamental planting. It is found in eastern Colorado at about 4,000 feet. It grows 1-2 feet tall, has attractive gray leaves and stems, with heads of indigo bloom in fall. It is very attractive in its season and has the whole show to itself when it blooms but is inconspicuous the rest of the year.

Amorphas have deep, tough roots and are hard to transplant. They are very tolerant of alkaline soils and drought.

Arctostaphylos uva-ursi, fruit and leaves

Arctostaphylos (Greek, bearberry) *uva-ursi* (Latin, bearberry).
KINNIKINNICK or BEARBERRY

This low, evergreen vine is a real soil maker and conservationist as it grows in very rocky, barren places and gradually helps soil to accumulate so that other plants may grow. It fills the soil with a network of roots and covers the surface with its mat of tiny, leathery leaves. It is one of the very few broadleaf evergreens that are able to survive our hot winter sun and dry air. It grows naturally in well-drained spots at elevations from 6,000-10,000 feet.

The tiny, pink and white, waxy, bell-shaped flowers appear from April to June, depending on location. The ¼ inch fruits that follow are green until fall and then bright-red over winter. Many birds and animals enjoy them, though they are a little dry and tasteless for human use. Indians used parts of the plant medicinally —the leaves to make tea or as a substitute for tobacco, to cure skins, and as a lotion for curing poisoning from poison oak. The leaves contain tannin. Pioneers made cider and jelly from the berries.

Because of its interlocking root system and its need for well-drained, slightly acid soil it is not used much as an ornamental ground cover. With more experience in methods of propagation it is sure to be more frequently used. Its greatest attraction is the sight of its green leaves and red berries peeking through the snow in winter.

Arctostaphylos patula   Arctostaphylos patula, berries

Arctostaphylos nevadensis coloradensis. PINE-MAT
MANZANITA

This species, intermediate between *A. patula* and *A. uva-ursi*, has been reported from northwestern Colorado at about 8,000 feet.

It grows from 1-2 feet tall in dense mats, with red berries and stems, with leaves and bloom a little larger than those of the kinnikinnick.

Arctostaphylos patula (spreading). GREENLEAF MANZANITA

Found occasionally in the southwestern part of the state, at 7,000-9,000 feet and plentifully in a few places, notably the Uncompahgre Plateau. It may grow in large solid stands, covering many square miles.

Its relationship to the familiar kinnikinnick may not at first be apparent, for it grows upright to several feet high and the leaves are larger. When it blooms the relationship is more noticeable, for it has a similar small, waxy, pink and white bloom.

The bark on the older stems is a rich mahogany-red and smooth, as though polished. Often these stems are grotesquely twisted and may be very attractive. The fruit is small, creamy-white to yellowish-brown, similar in size to that of the kinnikinnick and is eaten by several kinds of birds and animals.

This beautiful broadleaf evergreen requires a well-drained, rather acid soil and has deep roots, making it hard to transplant and grow under average conditions in the parts of the state where most of the population lives.

Artemisia sp. (mythological) SAGEBRUSH (Spanish, CHAMISO HEDIONDO) (see page 88)

Several shrubby species and many herbaceous kinds are found in the state. All but two alpine species grow in dry areas and have a distinctive odor. The Indians used the plants medicinally for many ailments, as they did almost any plant that had a strong or distinctive odor.

Artemisia tridentata (three-pointed leaf). BIG SAGEBRUSH or BLACK SAGE

This, with its many subspecies, is the most common shrubby kind. It grows all over the western and southwestern part of the state at altitudes of 5,000-9,500 feet. The most usual type is the *A. tridentata tridentata* which grows 3-12 feet tall depending on the richness of the soil. The early settlers soon learned to judge the quality of a soil by the height of the sagebrush. It often grows in almost solid stands, especially where there has been overgrazing. Many campers have found that the stems and roots used on a campfire give off a very disagreeable odor.

Three lower-growing subspecies are recognized:

A. tridentata rothrockii, grows 4-24 inches tall in parts of north-central and western Colorado, at 8,000-9,000 feet.

A. tridentata nova and *A. tridentata arbuscula* are under-shrubs, 4-12 inches tall, found rarely in western Colorado at about 7,500 feet.

Artemisia cana (white hairy) *viscidula* (sticky). SILVER or HAIRY SAGEBRUSH (see page 88)

This is generally a lower shrub than the big sagebrush, growing 1-6 feet tall. It is conspicuously silvery-hairy and has long, wedge-shaped, 3-pointed leaves similar to the big sagebrush. It is commonly found on the plains, hills, and valleys of the northwest part of the state, at elevations up to 10,000 feet. Often on north slopes or in protected places.

Artemisia filifolia (thread-leaf). SAND or THREADLEAF SAGE

This is a shrubby species, but generally lower. (1-4 feet tall). It is commonly found in sandy soil on the dry plains of the eastern slope, at altitudes of 3,500-5,500 feet. It has very narrow, 3-parted leaves, a silvery appearance and is often very beautiful with the sun shining on it, especially in the fall when it is full of the graceful seed stems.

Other low-growing, semi-shrubby species include:

Artemisia pedatifida (bird-footed leaf).

This is a rare sub-shrub, 2-6 feet tall, found on dry mesas of northwestern Colorado at 5,500 feet.

Artemisia frigida (of cold areas). FRINGED or MOUNTAIN SAGEBRUSH

This grows 4-14 inches tall, usually appearing herbaceous but often being definitely woody at base. Leaves are pinnately-parted and silvery gray and rather attractive. Scattered over the state up to 10,000 feet.

Artemisia tripartita or *trifida* (three-parted). THREE-TIP SAGEBRUSH

Grows 8-20 inches tall, similar to *A. tridentata*. May be found on dry, non-alkaline plains of northern Colorado at 8,000-9,000 feet.

Artemisia spinescens. BUD or **SPINY SAGEBRUSH** (see page 88)

A rounded, compact, spiny shrub under a foot high, with finely-dissected leaves, woody at the base. Found on dry, alkaline plains of the western slope at altitudes of 4,500-8,000 feet. It is a very different and distinctive little shrub when covered in early spring with masses of small, yellow flowers.

Artemisia bigelovii. FLAT SAGEBRUSH

Grows 8-12 inches tall on rocky banks and hills of central Colorado, at around 5,000 feet.

Two introduced species occasionally may be found naturalized around old settlements:

Artemisia absinthium (produces absinthe) and *A. abrotanum* (old man). These are partly woody, 1-6 feet high, sometimes used as hedges or specimens.

Sage is eaten by deer, grouse, rabbits, sheep and cattle when other foliage is scarce and is often the only thing to keep them alive in bad years. The flowers and seeds are very small and not conspicuous except when formed in large heads. One of the most important uses of sage by settlers was as a substitute for toilet paper.

The "purple sage" of the desert is not an *Artemisia* but belongs to the other sages or *Salvias*.

Aster sp. ASTER

Several of the asters have woody bases and so might be considered as shrubs:

A. arenosus, grows 2-4 inches tall, with solitary white flowers. It is found in dry areas over Colorado at 4,000-8,000 feet.

A. coloradoënsis, grows 2-4 inches tall, with violet flowers, at 9,000-11,000 feet.

A. glabriuscula, grows 4-8 inches tall, with clustered white and pink flowers, in rocky, clay soil, at 5,000-6,000 feet.

A. venustus, grows 8-15 inches tall, with solitary flowers of white, rose, or purple. It is found on the dry plains of western Colorado, at 4,500-7,000 feet.

Atriplex sp. SALTBRUSHES (Spanish, CHAMISO or
ORACHE) (see page 88)

There are three or more species found in the state which have
stems persistent or woody enough to be classed as shrubs:

Atriplex canescens (gray-hairy). FOUR-WING SALTBRUSH,
CHICO, or HOARY SALTBRUSH

This is a shrub 2-4 feet tall, with silvery or scurfy leaves and
stems. It is found growing alone or mixed with other desert
shrubs on shale or clay, alkaline or non-alkaline soils of the
desert or plains.

Atriplex confertifolia (crowded leaf) SHADSCALE or
ROUNDLEAF SALTBRUSH

This is a smaller, spiny shrub.

Atriplex nuttallii. NUTTALL SALTBRUSH

This is a still lower shrub, growing about a foot high.

All are shrubs of the desert or dry, clay soils. In favorable places
they may be very common or mixed with other desert plants. The
bloom is small and ordinarily inconspicuous. The fruit is small and
winged, usually green but sometimes brown or red. The foliage has
a slightly salty taste which gives the plant its name.

These plants are palatable to only a few animals and appear to
have little economic value except to hold the soil and give shelter
to desert wildlife. The seeds were gathered and eaten by Indians.

Baccharis sp. (from Bacchus). GROUNDSEL TREE, DESERT
BROOM (see page 88)

Usually a tall, willow-like shrub, growing in moist, saline soil
but occasionally seen as a more dwarfed shrub in drier locations.
Willow-like leaves and small, greenish-white, composite flowers in
terminal tassels, May-July, the staminate and pistillate on separate
plants. Seed heads of staminate and pistillate plants are different
but often appear like little cotton balls. Stems green, often striated,
smooth, often sticky with a resin-like substance. Two shrubby
species may be found in the southern part of the state:

Baccharis salicina (salty). WILLOW BACCHARIS

Baccharis emoryi. EMORY BACCHARIS, WATERWILLOW

These are found at low altitudes and may grow 3-8 feet tall. The
Cimarron River bottoms, in the extreme southeast corner of the
state, are covered with *Baccharis*.

Two species that are woody only at the base may also be found occasionally in southwestern Colorado at altitudes around 5,000 feet:

Baccharis wrightii. WRIGHT BACCHARIS, a low-branching, shrubby plant.

Baccharis glutinosa (sticky). SEEPWILLOW, a taller plant with simple stems.

Berberis fendleri. COLORADO or FENDLER'S BARBERRY (see page 89)

This shrub may be found in sunny places in southwestern Colorado. It is a plant of the foothills rather than the desert. It grows about 2-4 feet tall. It bears drooping clusters of small, yellow flowers in May and June, and these are followed by red berries which ripen in September. The growth is much like the common eastern barberry, but smaller. Spiny stems, purplish-brown and shiny; leaves small and spiny, apparently simple.

This would make an attractive cultivated shrub, but it is supposed to be one of the alternate hosts of the wheat rust and so is banned from cultivation.

Berberis or *Mahonia fremontii.* FREMONT MAHONIA, FREMONT BARBERRY, DESERT BARBERRY (Spanish, PALO AMARILLO (see page 89)

A broadleaf evergreen shrub, growing 5-10 feet tall, coming into the state occasionally from the southwest. The leaves are compound, consisting of 3-7 leaflets, about an inch long, half as wide, net-veined, and spiny, resembling small holly leaves. The flowers are small, yellow balls in clusters, appearing in May-June, and the fruits that follow are about the same size, blue, dry, and edible. A yellow dye is made from the stems and roots, and the berries were also used by the Indians for a blue paint. It is similar in habit to the red holly-grape of Utah but is distinguished from that plant by smaller, broader leaves and blue berries.

Berberis or *Mahonia haematocarpa* (blood-fruit). RED HOLLY-GRAPE (see page 89)

This tall, evergreen shrub occasionally comes into the state from Utah. Similar in general habit to Fremont mahonia of New Mexico but distinguished from it by the evergreen leaflets, which are more than an inch long, shiny, and quite narrow, and by the fruits, which are ¼-½ inch in diameter, bright-red, juicy, and very tasty. Local Indians call the plant "we-up." It is supposed to be a carrier of the wheat rust and so is banned from cultivated use.

Berberis repens, bloom

Berberis repens, fruit

Berberis or *Mahonia repens* or *aquifolium*. CREEPING MAHONIA, OREGON GRAPE, HOLLY-GRAPE (Spanish, YERBA DE LA SANGRE)

A beautiful ground cover found all through the mountains and foothills to 10,000 feet, usually on steep slopes where the drainage is good. Seldom over a foot high and spreading from connected underground runners. The leaves are evergreen, compound, bright-green, twisted, and spiny, resembling holly. They change to various shades of red in fall, depending on how much sun hits them.

The flowers appear very early in spring, sometimes even in March on sunny slopes. They consist of clusters of small, round, yellow bloom, each about ½ inch across. The fruits are about the same size as the bloom, appearing in fall as blue-black berries. These fruits are eaten by some birds and mammals but are a little too bitter for human use except when made into jelly.

Because this plant thrives in loose soil and rock and spreads so readily, it is a valuable soil binder. The stems are yellow inside and were used by the Indians for dye. They appear to have some medicinal value. A hillside covered with Oregon grape in winter is a beautiful sight, and choice stems may be collected for indoor decoration at Christmastime with very little damage to the plant. It transplants with great difficulty.

Betula glandulosa. BOG BIRCH (see page 89)

A beautiful little shrub, often found growing with willow in boggy places or along streams from 9,000-11,000 feet. It is usually a well-shaped shrub from 3-5 feet tall. The leaves are small, round in outline, toothed, and dark-leathery appearing. It has brown, cherry-like, glandular bark. The male bloom-catkins expand in early spring, followed by the female catkins which form the seed and hang on for months, looking much like miniature spruce cones.

This plant might make a beautiful ornamental shrub but because it requires a boggy soil and its roots are very sensitive to drying out, it does not transplant easily.

Betula occidentalis (western) or *fontinalis* (of spring). WATER or ROCKY MOUNTAIN BIRCH (see page 89)

An attractive, large shrub of the montane and foothills zones, up to 9,000 feet. Always found growing in moist places, usually along streams and often associated with its near relative the thin-leaf alder, or various willows.

Usually seen growing in clumps 6-8 feet tall but will sometimes grow up to 15 feet and more, with almost tree-like trunks. This plant is confusing to strangers from the East because they expect to find white bark on all birch trees, and this species always has a red-brown, cherry-like bark. Pronounced lenticels on the bark and "pitch" spots on the very slender twigs help to identify it.

The leaves are ovate, toothed, 1-2 inches long. The male bloom-catkins develop in early spring and disappear after blooming, then the female seed "cones" develop through the summer, eventually forming little catkins much resembling miniature spruce cones.

This shrub makes a nice, tall, ornamental plant when nursery grown and carefully transplanted. The only safe time to transplant it is in May, just as the buds show green.

Brickellia sp. BRICKELLBUSH, THOROUGHWORT

There are five species of *Brickellia* found generally in western Colorado that might be classed with the shrubs. These grow 1-3 feet tall and are woody at the base or part way up. The hanging, dirty-white, rayless disc flowers bloom in fall. They are distinctive, with triangular leaves, and grow from the mountains to the plains.

Ceanothus fendleri, bloom

Ceanothus fendleri. FENDLER CEANOTHUS, NEW JERSEY TEA

A low, spiny shrub, growing on steep, well-drained, rocky slopes at altitudes of 6,000-8,000 feet. Blooms in June with heads of small, white flowers sometimes completely covering the plant. The leaves are small and partly evergreen. Fruit inconspicuous. Some winters will kill back severely. This transplants with difficulty or it would make a valuable rock-garden plant. In spite of the spines it is occasionally eaten by porcupines, deer, and domestic livestock.

Ceanothus ovatus (egg shaped) or *mollissimus* (very soft hairy). INLAND CEANOTHUS or REDROOT

Various authorities list a native *Ceanothus* midway between *C. velutinus* and *C. fendleri.* There are occasional specimens, found at around 6,000 feet, that resemble more nearly one or the other. These may be of a separate species, but it is more likely that most of them are hybrids. As far as is known, they are nowhere plentiful. Some form well-shaped shrubs 3 or 4 feet tall, and when blooming in May and June, with white flower heads, may resemble spirea. They prefer well-drained, acid soil and have such deep roots that they have seldom been successfully transplanted.

Ceanothus velutinus, forest habitat

Ceanothus velutinus, seed capsules

Ceanothus velutinus (velvety). SNOWBRUSH CEANOTHUS, MOUNTAIN BALM (see page 89)

One of the most conspicuous of our native broadleaf evergreens. Not generally distributed over the area, but found occasionally on steep slopes at 6,000-10,000 feet, mainly in north-central parts of the state. Sometimes in quite dense patches, as on Rabbit Ears Pass. Forms a shrub 1-3 feet tall. Younger stems greenish and older stems dark.

Leaves deep green and glistening, sticky and balsam-fragrant, remaining on the stems all winter. Bloom in June and July consisting of large elongated heads of small, white flowers sometimes almost covering the plants. Fruit in dry capsules.

Grows in well-drained, acid soil and has a deep, woody root system. It would make a wonderful cultivated shrub if some way could be devised to propagate it and soil could be prepared to suit it.

Leaves and bloom of this species, and to some extent other species, make a very acceptable tea.

Celtis occidentalis (western). COMMON HACKBERRY (see page 92)

This is generally a tree, growing in the foothills, plains, mesas, or canyons at 4,000-7,500 feet, but where it gets little water it may become a dwarfed, picturesque shrub. The bark is light gray and corky, the bloom tiny and inconspicuous, and the fruits are small, dark berries. These berries hang on for a long time and have a pleasant, sweetish taste when chewed, though they are little more than a skin stretched over a hard seed. The leaves somewhat resemble those of the American elm but are paler and more lop-sided.

This is a most valuable tree for dry, alkaline conditions, but it is a little hard to transplant. It is subject to disfiguring galls on the stems and leaves.

Cercis occidentalis. WESTERN REDBUD (see page 92)

A large shrub or small tree with heart-shaped leaves. The bloom is bud-like, of a distinctive pink-purple in very early spring. The fruits are brown "pea-pods" that hang on in clusters all winter. It may seem surprising to find redbud growing in Utah canyons when it is thought of as a tree of the Southeast. It may come into Colorado from the southwest in remote canyons.

Cercocarpus montanus, bloom   Cercocarpus montanus, seed

Cercocarpus ledifolius

Cercocarpus (tailed fruit) *ledifolius* (leaf like Ledum). CURL-LEAF MOUNTAIN MAHOGANY (Spanish, PALO DURO)

Except for the bloom and fruit this shrub does not much resemble the common mountain mahogany. It frequently grows 8 feet tall or more, sometimes in almost impenetrable stands. The leaves are small, very narrow, dark green above and light below, slightly curled; they remain on the plant for two years. Blooms in July are small reddish tubes. Fruits have typical twisted tails. Comes into the state largely from Utah on the southwest. It is of little economic value, but as it often holds its foliage over the winter and becomes a well-shaped shrub, it has great ornamental possibilities. Methods of propagation need to be worked out.

86

Cercocarpus intricatus (much branched). LITTLELEAF MOUNTAIN MAHOGANY

A low, densely-branched shrub with narrow, curled, leathery leaves. Found occasionally in the western part of the state at elevations of 4,000-5,000 feet. Fruits and flowers similar to other *Cercocarpus*.

The Navajo Indians used a concoction of the root of these plants, mixed with the ashes of juniper and the powdered bark of alder to make a red dye for wool. The wood was used for implements before iron was introduced, as it is very hard.

Cercocarpus montanus or *parvifolius* (few-leaved). TRUE MOUNTAIN MAHOGANY or FEATHERBUSH

This shrub covers many dry, sunny hillsides in the montane and foothills zones. It is often associated with scrub oak or serviceberry and in favored spots with wax currant, chokecherry, mountain spirea or snowberry. It generally appears as a sparse shrub of irregular shape, growing 4-6 feet tall. The leaves are small, wedge-shaped, toothed, and almost evergreen. The flowers in May consist of small, greenish tubes with red ends. The seeds, which have long, fuzzy, corkscrew-twisted tails, hang on all winter and give the plant a very attractive appearance, especially with the sun shining through them.

It is browsed by some wild animals and domestic stock and makes a rather attractive shrub for dry places, as it thickens up and becomes more symmetrical under cultivation.

Chamaebatiaria (like a bramble) *millefolium* (thousand-leaf). FERNBUSH or TANSYBUSH (see page 109)

An aromatic shrub of the desert. In the rose family with such as the *Spiraeas* and *Sorbarias*. Has finely-divided leaves and small white flowers in large terminal clusters, June to August. Not generally distributed but probably comes into the state from the southwest.

Chimaphila umbellata occidentalis. WESTERN PIPSISSEWA

This is a low plant (4-8 inches) with short, woody stems that might classify it with the shrubs. Found occasionally in well-drained, shady spots in the montane and subalpine areas. It has rosettes of dark, leathery leaves, and short stems of beautiful, waxy, purple-lavender bloom in summer.

Baccharis **sp.** (p. 80)

Baccharis **sp.** (p. 80)

Artemisia **sp.** (p. 77)

Artemisia spinescens (p. 79)

Artemisia cana viscidula (p. 78)

Atriplex **sp.** (p. 80)

erberis fendleri (p. 81)

Betula occidentalis (p. 83)

3etula glandulosa (p. 83)

Ceanothus velutinus (p. 85)

Berberis haematocarpa (p. 81)

Chrysothamnus sp. (gold shrub). RABBIT BRUSH or
RUBBER SHRUB, GOLDENBUSH (Spanish, CHAMISO
BLANCO) (see page 109)

The rabbit brushes are typical desert plants, but also grow along
roads and in neglected corners adjacent to irrigated areas. They
are unpalatable to wildlife and domestic livestock, which only eat
them because of scarcity of other forage. They are sometimes
considered as indicators of overgrazing.

The plants are not conspicuous throughout summer, but in fall
when they are covered with their yellow, goldenrod-like flowers,
they are really beautiful. The leaves are slender, 2-3 inches long,
and sharp-pointed. The lower stems are woody and gray, while
the upper ones are green and gray-wooly or smooth. They are
deep-rooted and hard to transplant, as are most of the desert
shrubs.

Indians made a yellow dye from the flowers and used the stems
medicinally and to thatch roofs.

Chrysothamnus nauseosus (nauseating) or *graveolens* (heavy-
scented). GREENPLUME RABBIT BRUSH

This is the most common species in the area, found over the
plains and foothills, mesas and desert, along roads and on hillsides. This one grows to a height of 3-5 feet. It contains 2% to
6% rubber.

Chrysothamnus parryi. PARRY RABBIT BRUSH

This is less shrubby, has larger leaves and smaller, paler flowers.

Chrysothamnus viscidiflorus (sticky leaves). DOUGLAS RABBIT
BRUSH

This is another species found west of the Rockies.

Chrysothamnus depressus (low). DWARF RABBIT BRUSH

This may occasionally be found, also *C. vaseyi, C. greenei, C.
pulchellus* (beautiful) and many subspecies. Specific names have
been assigned by various authorities to a great many variations
found over the area so that there is little uniformity in nomenclature.

Clematis pseudoalpina

Clematis, seed head

Clematis ligusticifolia (strap-shaped leaf). WESTERN
VIRGIN'S BOWER

A semi-woody vine found growing in the foothills and into the plains, mountains, and mesas. Often growing over hawthorn, chokecherry, wild plum, and other tall shrubs along streams and on fences. May grow 10-20 feet in a season in favorable locations. The leaves are compound and clasping, the flowers are white, star-like in clusters, and the fruits are in attractive fuzzy heads that remain all winter. It is similar to the eastern clematis, *C. paniculata* but is slightly hardier in our climate, not fragrant, blooming in the spring.

Indians and pioneers made many medicinal uses of the leaves, seeds, and stems.

Clematis orientalis. ORIENTAL CLEMATIS or YELLOW
CLEMATIS

A hardy vine that has been introduced into the state, notably near Idaho Springs. It has naturalized itself in the last 50 years along roads and up streams where it forms dense tangles in some areas. It bears attractive yellow flowers, about 2 inches across, singly on long stems. The fuzzy or shiny seed heads remain on all winter and are very attractive. It usually sprawls over hillsides with vines 6-10 feet long.

Clematis pseudoalpina. ROCKY MOUNTAIN CLEMATIS

This is a frail, semi-woody vine, seldom much branched or over 5 feet long, growing occasionally in moist, shady places in the foothills and mountains over the state.

The blooms are a beautiful lavender or occasionally white and may have a spread of 3 inches. They grow solitarily along the vine on long stems. Leaves are twice 3-parted.

91

Cercis occidentalis (p. 85)

Celtis occidentalis (p. 85)

Celtis occidentalis (p. 85)

Cowania mexicana (p. 94)

Cowania mexicana (p. 94)

Cowania mexicana (p. 94)

Clematis columbiana. COLUMBIAN ROCK CLEMATIS

Somewhat similar to the Rocky Mountain clematis, but the leaves are only once 3-parted. Occasionally found in north-central Colorado at altitudes of 6,000-10,000 feet.

Coleogyne (sheathed ovary) *ramosissima* (many-branched). BLACKBRUSH (see page 109)

Found singly or in solid stands in the desert areas of the southwest part of the state at 4,000-6,000 feet. Rather low-growing, wide-spreading, dense, with spiny-tipped, opposite branches. Showy yellow flowers in May and June. Small bunches of tiny, narrow leaves and inconspicuous fruits. It has no apparent value other than erosion control, the attractive bloom which lasts a few days, and very limited use as a forage for wildlife and domestic stock.

Cornus stolonifera coloradense, fruit

Cornus stolonifera (rooting by stolons) *coloradense.* COLORADO RED OSIER DOGWOOD

Found from the upper plains zone, through the foothills, mesas, and into the montane zone, growing along streams in moist places, usually associated with willows and sometimes birch, alder, and honeysuckle. It stands out in winter because of its bright-red stems. Blooms in spring, and sparingly throughout summer, with flat heads of tiny, white flowers, without the conspicuous white bracts of the flowering dogwood of the east. The fruits are small, juicy, white or lead-colored berries which often persist throughout winter and furnish an important food for some birds and animals. It usually grows from 4-6 feet tall, and, different from the eastern type, suckers but little.

This is one of our finest native shrubs for ornamental use. It is easily transplanted, readily started from cuttings, and can be sheared to keep it within bounds. The long, slim stems or "osiers" were used by the Indians for making baskets. Leaves and inner bark were used by Indians and early settlers as a substitute or adulterant for tobacco. It has a slightly narcotic effect which might be dangerous.

Cornus baileyi. BAILEY DOGWOOD

Reported to be found occasionally over much the same range as *C. stolonifera*, probably coming in from the east. It differs by having stems duller in color and leaves which are hairier.

Corylus cornuta, leaves and fruit

Corylus cornuta (horned) or *rostrata* (beaked). FILBERT or HAZEL-NUT

An attractive shrub in the birch family. Has light-brown, straight stems, usually growing 4-6 feet tall, found in dense thickets in moist, shady places, on the north slopes of small streams in the foothills of north-central Colorado.

The flowers are in catkins, the overwintering male blooming early in spring and the female gradually developing over the summer into long, husked nuts. It is seldom that the few nuts are left alone by squirrels long enough to ripen, but those found make excellent eating. The plant is not common and the fruits sparsely produced.

This is a slow-growing shrub, difficult to transplant, but making a nice ornamental when once established.

Cowania (after James Cowan) *mexicana* or *stansburiana*. CLIFFROSE or QUININEBUSH (see page 92)

A common shrub of dry areas in the southwestern part of the

94

state. Grows in rocky places at elevations of 4,000-8,000 feet. It sometimes gets to be 6 feet tall or more, with a large, contorted, woody stem but is most often seen as a nice shrub of about 4-5 feet.

When covered with yellow flowers in May, it is a beautiful plant. The flowers are like small, single roses, light yellow in color, and about ¾ inches across. The fruits are dry but have long, twisted, feathery tails attached, which give the plant in seed a clematis-like appearance. The leaves are very small, ⅓-½ inch long, wedge-shaped, 3-divided, leathery above and whitish below, almost evergreen. The bark is pale, gray-brown, and shreddy like a juniper, young twigs reddish-brown or greenish.

The soft, inner bark was used by some Indians to weave cloth, cordage, mats, and sandals. The leaves are very bitter but are eaten by deer and domestic stock in emergencies. This would make a very attractive, cultivated shrub for dry places.

Crataegus succulenta, bloom   Crataegus succulenta, fruit

Crataegus chrysocarpa (golden fruit). FIREBERRY HAWTHORN or THICKLEAVED HAWTHORN

This includes *C. doddsi, C. sheridana,* and *C. rotundifolia* of some authors.

A rare shrub with much the same range and habits of the fleshy hawthorn. Distinguished by its small, round, dry fruits, yellow to orange. The leaves are thick and round in outline with reddish glands on petioles and teeth. The twigs are generally reddish, with curved reddish thorns 1-1½ inches long.

Crataegus erythropoda or *cerronis.* SHINY-LEAVED or CERRO HAWTHORN

A small widely-branched tree or shrub, found in canyons and up

95

to 8,000 feet, mainly on the western slope. Twigs are brown; the leaves shiny, diamond-shaped, slightly lobed, thin. Spines numerous, morocco-red, about an inch long. Fruits brown or black, hard, ¼ inch long, eaten by birds. Bloom in flat heads of small, white flowers.

Crataegus rivularis or *wheeleri*. RIVER HAWTHORN
Small, well-branched tree with slender branchlets, coming into the state from the northwest corner. Few, slender spines, about an inch long, black, curved and glossy. Leaves ovate, about an inch wide and twice as long. Fruits small, dark-red to black.

Crataegus (ancient Greek, strength) *succulenta* (succulent fruit). FLESHY HAWTHORN or COLORADO HAWTHORN
This includes *C. occidentalis, C. coloradensis* and *C. coloradoides* of some authors.

The most common hawthorn of the streams and canyons of the eastern slope. Usually grows in tangled masses disliked by cowboys. Sometimes rather dull and gray in effect, but more often the stems are a glossy brown or yellowish color and attractive, even in winter. The thorns are few but stout, 1-1½ inches long. The leaves are wedge-shaped, dark green, shiny above and duller below. The distinguishing characteristic of the species (or group of species) is the bright-red, fleshy fruit, which is rather tasty. This fruit sometimes hangs on over part of the winter but is eaten sooner or later by wildlife. The flowers are small, white, in flat clusters on the ends of the twigs.

Its flowers, fruits, and bright twigs make it a valuable shrub for ornamental use. It is hard to transplant, slow-growing, and may be sheared in formal shapes.

Crataegus saligna (willow). WILLOW HAWTHORN
Found along streams in the west-central part of the state up to 7,000 feet, especially along the Gunnison River. A slender shrub or small tree, 6-10 feet high, with narrow, willow-like leaves and heads of white flowers in spring. The fruits are about ½ inch in diameter, blue-black, dry, and insipid. There are numerous, slender, black spines an inch long or more. The fruit is eaten by many birds and some animals. This plant has never been used much as an ornamental, but should be useful.

Desmanthus illinoensis and *cooleyi.* BUNDLE FLOWER (Pea family)

An herbaceous or partly-woody plant with pinnate leaves, small, slightly twisted pods and small, whitish or greenish flowers in heads or spikes. It may grow 8-18 inches tall, with erect stems. Occasionally found in eastern or southeastern Colorado at 3,500-4,500 feet.

Ditaxis humilis and *mercurialina.* (Spurge family)

A small, erect perennial, woody at the base, with purplish sap. The small flowers, staminate and pistillate, are in axillary clusters. It is occasionally found on the plains in southeastern Colorado at 3,500-4,000 feet.

Dryas octopetala. MOUNTAIN DRYAD, EIGHT-PETALLED DRYAD, WASHINGTON DRYAD, ALPINE AVENS, MOUNTAIN AVENS

Found on some mountains above timberline, in dense, ground-covering masses. It is woody at the base but seldom grows more than a few inches tall. It is distributed over many parts of the world at high altitudes. The flowers appear in July, singly, on upright stems, one inch across, made up of 8 or 9 white or cream-colored petals. The heads of fruit following the bloom have long feathery tails, much like clematis. The leaves are heavy, leathery, dark green above and white and hairy below, about one inch long and ⅓ inch wide with scalloped edges.

Echinocactus sp. BARREL CACTUS, HEDGEHOG CACTUS, DEVIL'S CLAW

The flowers appear at the top and the fruit is not spiny. The flowers may be colored pinkish, yellowish, or lavender-purple. The fruit is greenish or red. The sections are cylindrical, with vertical ribs.

Echinocactus whipplei

97

Echinocactus whipplei. DWARF BARREL CACTUS or
COMPASS PLANT
 Common in the southwestern part of the state. Grows 3-12 inches
high, generally leaning towards the south. Generally single plants
with rose-pink flowers.

Echinocereus sp. (hedgehog waxcandle). HEDGEHOG
CACTUS, KING'S CROWN, STRAWBERRY CACTUS
 There are at least 5 species of hedgehog cacti in the state and
much variation in nomenclature by different authorities. The color
of the bloom may vary from greenish-yellow to pink, red, and purple. The plants are ball-shaped with vertical or spiral ribs, the
flowers are at the sides, and the fruit is spiny.

Echinocereus coccineus. CLARET-CUP CACTUS
 Has scarlet bloom, is fairly small, ball-shaped, and often occurs
in large clusters. Found commonly in the southwestern part of the
state.

Elaeagnus (Greek, kind of olive) *angustifolia* (narrowleaf).
RUSSIAN OLIVE (see page 156)
 Russian olives have naturalized themselves all over the state,
along ravines at lower elevations where they can tolerate the
drought and alkalinity. They bear numerous, small, yellow flowers
in early spring and small, gray or brown "olives," which hang on
all winter and are eaten by waxwings in spring. The plants may
grow as bushy shrubs or tall trees, with gray, narrow leaves.

Elaeagnus commutata or *argentea.* SILVERBERRY
 This has naturalized itself in parts of Wyoming and may be
found in northern Colorado. There is one group along the highway just south of Antero Junction. Blooms in May or later. Bears
silvery fruits in October.

Eriogonum sp. WILD BUCKWHEAT, UMBRELLA PLANT
(see page 115)
 There are about 40 species of this genus reported in the state
which have woody bases from a short distance up the stem to over
half or three-quarters of the height. About a third of these are
mat-plants, under 4 inches tall, some are few-stemmed and tall,
but most of them run about a foot high and are densely-branched.

The flowers are tiny, in various-shaped heads, usually white, pink, or yellow and often with bare stems.

All are found growing in dry ground on plains, foothills, mesas, and deserts. The following are classed as shrubs by various authorities:

Eriogonum nebraskense, a shrub 6-12 inches tall with rose-colored flowers, found on the dry plains of southeastern Colorado.

Eriogonum microthecum, SLENDER BUCKWHEATBRUSH is listed by some.

Many of these are very attractive and would make valuable cultivated plants if methods of propagation could be developed.

Ephedra **sp.**, seed   Ephedra **sp.**

Ephedra sp. JOINTFIR, MORMON TEA, BRIGHAM TEA (Spanish, CANUTILLO DEL CAMPO)

This is a strange-looking shrub, found in dry or rocky places in the southwest, at elevations of 4,500-9,000 feet. The true leaves are very small and soon drop off, so the manufacture of food is done by the chlorophyll in the straight green stems.

The staminate and pistillate flowers are on separate plants. The staminate flowers, composed of clusters of stamens at the joints, are yellow and rather attractive, covering the plant in May. Later, the fruits form in a sheath of scales on the pistillate plants. These fruits, rather large, black nuts, much like beech nuts, are eaten by quail, antelope, ground squirrels, and other animals. They are edible by humans when roasted as the Indians did.

A rather palatable substitute for tea is made by steeping the stems in hot water (especially if plenty of lemon and sugar is used). The stems were chewed by the Indians to relieve thirst and have almost a raspberry taste. Concoctions made from this plant have been used medicinally for 5,000 years. It is grazed by wild and domestic animals.

Ephedra antisyphilitica, VINE EPHEDRA or CANATILLA is rather low and spreading, and has opposite stems.
Ephedra torreyana, TORREY EPHEDRA, *E. viridis*, GREEN EPHEDRA, and *E. trifurca*, LONGLEAF EPHEDRA or POPO-TILLO all have branches in threes and are upright shrubs 3-6 feet tall.

Eurotia lanata

Eurotia (mouldy) *lanata* (wooly). COMMON WINTERFAT or WHITE SAGE

This plant grows on the dry plains, foothills, and mesas in sandy alkaline soils at altitudes of 4,000-8,000 feet. It grows 1-3 feet tall and is woody at the base. Flowers are tiny and tufted, in the axils of the leaves. The seed plumes which follow have long, silky hairs. The leaves are thread-like, ½-2 inches long. The whole plant usually has a rather distinctive and attractive gray-wooly appearance but this may turn to golden-brown with age.

Considered as a valuable winter stock food. Attractive when used in dried winter arrangements. It was used medicinally by the Indians. It helps to control soil erosion as it has deep, spreading roots.

Fallugia paradoxa. APACHE PLUME, FEATHER-ROSE, (Spanish, PONIL) (see page 112)

This attractive shrub is not common in the state, but is found occasionally in the southwestern and south-central part, notably south of Sand Dunes National Monument. It grows in dry or sunny places, and its sparse, straggly growth and very small leaves give it the appearance of a desert plant. Its simultaneous show of white flowers and fuzzy seed heads throughout the summer make it a very attractive shrub. It will grow 3-5 feet tall, depending on the richness of the soil and availability of water. It has rather thin, branched, and scraggly stems with a whitish bark. The leaves are very small, wedge-shaped, almost evergreen, and pinnately divided into 3-7 divisions. The bloom is of white, 5-petalled, single flowers, an inch or more across, resembling single, white roses or thimbleberry bloom. These are borne erect on long stems. The small, dry fruit are in heads, and have long, wavy, silvery-to-purple, clematis-like plumes attached. This gives it its common name of Apache plume. The most interesting character of the shrub is its habit of being in both bloom and fruit all summer.

Some Indians used the stems for brooms and arrow-shafts; others used a brew from the leaves as a treatment for hair growth. It is valuable for winter forage, erosion control, and beauty, either naturally where it grows, or as a cultivated shrub for dry places.

Fendlera rupicola (growing on cliffs). FALSE MOCKORANGE or CLIFF FENDLERBUSH (see page 112)

Found in dry, sunny places, often among piñon and juniper, in southwestern and west-central Colorado. It is a rather neat, upright shrub with opposite stems and leaves. It is in the *Hydrangea* family along with the native *Jamesia* and *Philadelphus*. The small leaves are about an inch long, entire, narrow, thickish, and twisted. The bloom in May resembles that of the mockorange, small, about an inch across, white, 4-petalled, pink in bud, borne terminally in clusters of 3, solitarily. The seed pods are 4-divided, dry, and cup-shaped like the mockorange and remain on the plants all year long, helping in identification. It would make a nice ornamental shrub for dry places.

Fendlerella utahensis. LITTLE FENDLERBUSH (see page 112)

This is a small shrub in the *Saxifrage* family, very closely related to the *Philadelphus* and *Fendlera*. It forms a compact little shrub up to 3 feet tall, with many small leaves and mockorange-like flowers. It is only occasionally found in rocky canyons, in the northwestern corner of the state, at 5,000-8,000 feet. It is more common in parts of Utah and Arizona. The bark of the stems is shreddy. The blossoms are in few-flowered, compound cymes.

Forestiera neomexicana, Forestiera neomexicana, Forestiera neomexicana,
staminate bloom   pistillate bloom   fruit

Forestiera neomexicana. MOUNTAIN PRIVET, NEW
MEXICAN FORESTIERA, ADELIA, PALO BLANCO,
TANGLEBRUSH

This is found growing in unexpected and out-of-the-way places
in the southwestern corner of the state. Occasionally it predom-
inates, as along the lower Dolores River. It grows 4-12 feet tall,
depending on soil and water. It prefers places with some water
nearby, though it tolerates much heat. The stems are opposite,
like ash, but the general growth and leaves more resemble privet.
The staminate and pistillate flowers are on separate plants. The
flowers are small and yellow and appear before the leaves. The
fruits on the pistillate plants are small, black berries with a whitish
"bloom," sometimes in large, attractive clusters in the fall. The
wood is tough and was used by the Indians for their digging sticks.

It makes a neat ornamental shrub for dry places, either trimmed
or growing naturally.

Forsellesia meionandra (small stamens). GREASEBUSH
(Bittersweet family) (see page 109)

This is a small, intricately-branched shrub up to 20 inches high,
with greenish, spiny, angled stems. The leaves are very numerous
and tiny, round and almost evergreen. Flowers are solitary. Found
in the hills and deserts of southwestern Colorado at 4,500-7,000
feet.

Forsellesia spinescens. GREASEBUSH

This grows in the same location as *F. meionandra* but is about
twice the size with leaves several times as long. It is a looser-
growing shrub. It may be scattered with other desert shrubs or
sometimes may be the dominant shrub.

Frankenia jamesii. PEARLY MOCKHEATHER

(The only genus and species in the family, between *Tamarix* and *Hypericum.*)

Erect shrubs, 8-24 inches tall, with branches fascicled. Small, white flowers, fruit a capsule, small linear leaves. Occasionally found in the Arkansas River Valley and southwestern Colorado at 4,000-5,500 feet.

Fraxinus anomala

Fraxinus anomala, "canoe-paddles"

Fraxinus anomala, old trunk

Fraxinus anomala. SINGLELEAF ASH, DWARF ASH

Grows on canyon slopes in the southwestern and west-central parts of the state. A rather thin, scraggly shrub, up to 20 feet tall. Sometimes becomes almost a tree with trunk up to 8 inches in diameter. Ash-gray twigs, 4-angled, opposite, orange when young. Older bark furrowed and gray. Bloom small, greenish, in clusters in May. Fruits are pendant clusters of broad-winged "canoe paddles." Leaves roundish, 1-2 inches across, single and simple, dark above and paler below.

This should be a valuable small ornamental tree for dry places.

Gaultheria humifusa. WESTERN, AROMATIC or CREEPING WINTERGREEN (see page 176)

A very low, creeping plant of the heath family, growing occasionally in moist, shady places in the subalpine zone, mainly in the north-central part of the state. It is seldom noticed except when the small, bright-scarlet fruit is ripe. This has a pleasant flavor and is relished by various wild birds and animals. The flowers are tiny, drooping, waxy-white or pinkish bells. The leaves are roundish, ¼ inch across, leathery, and evergreen.

103

Grayia brandegei. SPINELESS HOP-SAGE

Similar to *G. spinosa*, but a smaller shrub, spineless, with narrower leaves, fruits less than ¼ inch in diameter. Restricted to certain desert areas in the western part of the state.

Grayia spinosa. SPINY HOP-SAGE

A small, much-branched, spinose shrub, 1-3 feet high, in the goosefoot family, closely related to the saltbrushes and greasewood. Grows in dry, alkaline soils over much of the western foothills and canyon country. Has a gray appearance with touches of pink occasionally in the leaves and fruit. The bloom is rather inconspicuous, in terminal clusters. Fruits form broad-winged scales, ¼ inches or more wide. Leaves small, fleshy-mealy, spatulate to obovate. The plant is eaten by all stock and is supposed to be quite fattening.

Gutierrezia lucida or *sarothrae.* SNAKEWEED, BROWNWEED, TURPENTINE WEED

These are low, compact, much-branched plants, appearing as perennials but with woody bases. They grow from 6 inches to 18 inches tall, generally about a foot high. They have many small, narrow leaves and small, inconspicuous, composite yellow flowers in heads clustered near the ends of the branches. They are found very commonly on dry mesas at 4,000-8,000 feet, largely in the western part of the state or on eastern plains.

Haploesthes greggii. (Composite family)

A perennial or undershrub with linear-filiform, fleshy leaves. Stems are leafy, the ray flowers few and yellow. It may be found in southeastern Colorado.

Haplopappus (*Aplopappus*) sp. GOLDENWEED

Of some 28 species listed as occurring in the state, at least 7 are subshrubs or are woody at the base and so might be classed with the shrubs. Most species have yellow, ray flowers, but several are rayless. Some grow up to 2 feet tall, and others may be mat-plants under 3 inches high. Most have resinous or glandular leaves.

H. nuttallii, NUTTALL GOLDENWEED, has no rays, grows 4-12 inches tall and is found at 4,000-8,000 feet in western Colorado.

H. macronema, WHITESTEM GOLDENWEED, has no rays, grows 6-18 inches tall and is found from 9,000-12,000 feet in central Colorado.

H. engelmannii has no rays, grows 4-12 inches tall in eastern Colorado.

H. spinulosus, IRONPLANT GOLDENWEED, has yellow rays, grows 8-24 inches tall in southwestern and central Colorado.

H. fremontii, LEAFY BIGHEAD GOLDENWEED, has yellow rays, grows 6-12 inches tall and is found in southeastern Colorado.

H. acaulis, STEMLESS GOLDENWEED, is a woody mat-plant with yellow rays, growing 1-3 inches tall in northwestern Colorado, at 5,000-9,000 feet.

H. armerioides is also a woody mat-plant, growing 2-6 inches tall in western Colorado. Other species may occasionally be woody enough at the base to be classed as shrubs.

Helianthemum bicknellii. FROSTWEED (Rockrose family)

A perennial, woody at the base, growing 7-15 inches tall.

It has small, yellow flowers of two kinds, with 5 petals. It is found occasionally in dry areas in central Colorado at 7,000-7,500 feet. (*Lechia* is a similar genus with flowers 3-petalled and not yellow.)

Holodiscus dumosus, on hillside

Holodiscus dumosus, bloom

Holodiscus (entire disc) *dumosus* (shrubby). BUSH ROCK SPIREA, MOUNTAIN SPRAY, MEADOWSWEET, SHRUBBY CREAMBUSH

An attractive native shrub, closely related to our cultivated spireas. It grows 3-6 feet tall with straight stems and is usually a well-shaped plant. Found on steep, canyon slopes in the foothills and mesas at 6,000-9,000 feet, sometimes scattered but often in almost solid stands. The leaves are small, wedge-shaped, toothed, smooth above and white-hairy beneath.

This shrub does not attract attention except when it blooms in summer, at which time it is covered with large, pyramidal heads of small flowers, white to slightly cream or pink. When the leaves are bruised in stepping through a stand, for instance, they give off a pleasant "green apple" odor and this serves to identify the plant. The fruit itself is inconspicuous, but the white feathery bloom and seed heads remain on the plants most of the year, serving as a further identification.

A similar but smaller species, *Holodiscus microphyllus*, is reported coming into the state from the west. Jamesia americana

Jamesia americana. CLIFF JAMESIA, WAXFLOWER, CLIFFBUSH, MOUNTAIN MOCKORANGE, WILD HYDRANGEA

One of the most attractive of our native shrubs. Commonly found growing in cracks of rocks or in well-drained places where the roots can go down to moist soil. Found mainly in the montane zone but may occasionally be found in the foothills or subalpine zones. Grows 3-6 feet high. Has dark-green, thickish, deeply-veined, opposite leaves, fuzzy-white underneath. The small opposite twigs are fuzzy-white, shading to brown. The larger stems have peeling brown and gray bark. Irregularly branched but generally an attractive shape.

Flowers in terminal clusters, white and waxy, resembling orange blossoms, from May to July depending on season and altitude. The dry, brown seed heads, hanging on all winter, help in identification.

It is not easy to transplant as it requires a well-drained, acid soil and has deep roots. As it does not propagate readily, small plants are seldom found. In a suitable place it makes a very fine ornamental shrub.

106

Juniperus communis,
fruit and 3-striped needles

Juniperus monosperma

Juniperus utahensis

Juniperus utahensis, berries

Juniperus scopulorum,
in habitat

Juniperus scopulorum,
in town

Juniperus communis, or *sibirica*, vars. *montana* or *saxatilis.*
LOW JUNIPER, MOUNTAIN COMMON JUNIPER,
DWARF JUNIPER

Found from the foothills to above timberline as solitary specimens or in dense groups. Low and spreading, seldom over 3 feet
high but often spreading for 10 feet or more. Sometimes seen as
attractive, dense clumps and sometimes as scraggly, open plants.
Growing often in partial shade, under pines, but sometimes in the
open. Bright green throughout summer and fall but often badly
discolored or winterburned by spring in places where the sun hits
it.

The needles are single, about ⅔ inches long, very stiff and sharp
and arranged in whorls of three, appearing dark green above with
two distinctive white lines underneath. The fruits consists of bluish,
stemless berries about ¼ inch in diameter with 1-3 seeds in each.
These take three years to mature and may hang on the plants for
a couple of years after that.

This is a useful evergreen shrub when planted informally in
partly shaded places. It varies greatly in color and form, but all
discovered so far are inclined to winterburn so badly as to spoil
their beauty by spring.

Juniperus horizontalis or *sabina.* CREEPING JUNIPER

A low, creeping ground cover which has been reported coming
into the state from Wyoming. Selections from this species have
been made and named and proven valuable additions to the list of
evergreens suitable for ornamental plantings.

Juniperus monosperma (one-seed) or *mexicana.* CHERRY-
STONE JUNIPER, ONE-SEED JUNIPER (Spanish,
ALMACIGA DE SABINA)

A tree of the desert and semi-desert country of the southwestern
part of the state, usually found in association with the piñon pine.
Grows in dry, thin, usually clay soil at altitudes of 5,000-7,000
feet.

A small tree, generally 8-15 feet tall but sometimes growing up
to 30 feet. Generally about ⅔ as broad as it is high. Often many-
stemmed and irregular in shape. Older specimens usually retain
dead branches.

The fruits are berries ⅛ to ¼ inch in diameter and containing
just one seed, which matures in one year. The berries are suc-

Chrysothamnus **sp.** (p. 90)

Chamaebatiaria millefolium (p. 87)

Coleogyne ramosissima (p. 93)

Chamaebatiaria millefolium (p. 87)

Forsellesia meionandra (p. 102)

Lycium pallidum (p. 118)

culent, usually coppery but sometimes bluish in color. Needles are small, scale-like, and usually pale yellowish-green but sometimes blue-green. Bark of trunk and limbs gray-brown and fibrous, becoming very thick in old trees.

It is useful as an ornamental where a low, slow-growing tree is wanted. It will tolerate more drought and alkaline soil than the Colorado juniper and is more suitable for making a clipped hedge under difficult conditions. It is cut by ranchers for fence posts as it resists decay for many years. Excellent for fireplace fuel as it burns well and gives off a pleasant odor. Seeds eaten by birds and wild animals. The primitive Indians used the fruit for food, the bark for padding and beds, and the wood for fuel. They also made medicinal use of it.

Some authorities list an additional species found in the southwestern part of the state, *Juniperus gymnocarpa*, OPENSEED JUNIPER. This species is not readily distinguishable from the above.

Juniperus scopulorum (of the mountains). COLORADO JUNIPER, COLORADO CEDAR, SILVER CEDAR, ROCKY MOUNTAIN RED CEDAR, ROCKY MOUNTAIN JUNIPER
(Also known in the nursery trade as "scop.")

Found in open stands on dry, sunny hillsides or occasionally under other trees. Usually at an altitude of 5,000-7,000 feet and chiefly on the eastern slope, though occasional specimens are found in the southwest.

The shape varies from a symmetrical, pyramidal, dense, one-stemmed tree to a dwarfed, scraggly, many-stemmed shrub. The usual size is from 8-15 feet high but it may grow to a tree of 50 feet in a favorable location.

Fruit is a berry, about ¼ inch in diameter, blue-black to silvery-blue, covered with a blue-gray "bloom." These are borne only on the pistillate trees and take two years to mature. Edible but not very tasty.

Leaves are evergreen, very short or scale-like, covering the branchlets, colored from brownish-green through various shades of green to silvery-blue. Sometimes very attractive. Bark gray-brown, scaly, becoming thick, fibrous and ridged. Twigs usually slim, upturned and graceful.

Very valuable for long-lasting fence posts. Has dense, red wood, and sometimes lighter sapwood. One of the most valuable of the

110

native evergreens for ornamental use. It grows slowly and tolerates some shearing and can be kept in proportion to a small house for many years. The trees raised from collected seeds vary greatly in color, form, and rate of growth, so it is becoming more and more common to use grafts from trees of known quality. The wood has a very pleasant fragrance when used as firewood. The primitive Indians ate the berries, burned the wood, and used the shredded bark for beds.

Juniperus utahensis. UTAH JUNIPER, DESERT JUNIPER

A dwarf tree usually under 20 feet high, several-stemmed, slightly higher than it is broad, often with many dead limbs. It is found scattered over the western third of the state on dry mesas and along canyons from 5,000-9,000 feet, often associated with piñon pine.

Its general appearance is similar to the cherrystone juniper of the southwestern part of the state, but the berries are larger and fibrous rather than juicy, sometimes reddish-brown and sometimes a glistening blue-gray. The branches usually come from above ground level rather than below as with the cherrystone juniper. The needles also seem coarser.

It was much used by the Indians for hogan frames, firewood, and ladders, while the shredded bark made beds and helped to thatch shelters. The berries were used for food, and brews made from the twigs, or smoke from their burning, had many medicinal values, real or imaginary.

Kalmia polifolia, bloom

Fallugia paradoxa (p. 100)

Fallugia paradoxa (p. 100)

Fendlera rupicola (p. 101)

Fendlera rupicola (p. 101)

Fendlerella utahensis (p. 101)

Populus tremuloides (p. 127)

Kalmia polifolia (whitish leaves) or *microphylla*. BOG KALMIA, MOUNTAIN LAUREL, DWARF MOUNTAIN LAUREL, PALE LAUREL, SWAMP LAUREL

Our native *Kalmia* is a very low, woody, ground cover, found rarely in the subalpine zone around 10,000-11,000 feet, in swampy places along streams or on lake shores.

When in bloom in July, it is very attractive with its heads of small rose-purple flowers. Leaves about ½ inch long, rolled at the edges to appear narrow and willow-like. They are evergreen, dark and leathery above but pale beneath. Poisonous when eaten by stock, but not common enough to be a hazard.

Larrea or *Covillea tridentata, glutinosa* or *divaricata*. CREOSOTE BUSH (Spanish, HEDIONDILLA)

A distinctive shrub of the dry plains and mesas in the southwest, coming into the state occasionally from New Mexico. Grows 4-10 feet tall, depending on soil and rainfall, and is one of the last species of plants surviving in the most arid areas. The evergreen leaves are made up of two tiny (¼ inch) leaflets, yellowish-green, set on the short, jointed twigs in dense clusters. This makes the shrub stand out against the gray desert soil.

The distinctive creosote odor, especially after rains, is another identifying feature. Bloom is of tiny, yellow flowers in April or occasionally later. Fruits consist of five small nutlets which are formed in fuzzy, white seed balls. These nutlets are eaten by squirrels and rabbits, but the forage is poisonous to some livestock. It was used medicinally by the Indians and Mexicans; recent interest has been stimulated by the report that drinking a tea made from the leaves has reduced cancer. The whole shrub is very flammable.

Leptodactylon pungens. FALSE JUNIPER

These are low to very low plants, generally with densely-branched stems, covered with tiny leaves resembling juniper. They are evergreen and largely woody. The flowers in spring are a dirty-white and resemble the trailing phlox. Growing on mesas and canyons of the southwest under piñon and juniper (quite common in some areas). There are other species found occasionally in the north and on the plains.

Picea pungens (p. 125)

Picea engelmannii (p. 125)

Pseudotsuga taxifolia (p. 132)

Pinus aristata (p. 125)

Pinus ponderosa (p. 126)

Pinus contorta latifolia (p. 125)

Pinus flexilis (p. 126)

Pinus edulis (p. 126)

Populus sargentii (p. 127)

Populus angustifolia (p. 127)

Eriogonum sp. (p. 98)

Eriogonum sp. (p. 98)

Leptodactylon, flowers

Linnaea borealis or *americana.* AMERICAN TWINFLOWER

This is such a tiny, low plant that it is hard to think of it as one of the woody shrubs. However, it does have slim, creeping, woody stems which form mats covering the ground and old logs in damp, shady forests of the montane zone, from 6,000-10,000 feet. The leaves are ¼ to ¾ inches, almost round, evergreen, leathery, light green. The flowers are tiny, pink, waxy bells, hanging in pairs from the top of a slender stem about 2 inches tall. They may be located, when in bloom, by a delicate, all-pervading fragrance. Some think this is the most delicately beautiful of all wild flowers, and the famous Swedish botanist Linnaeus, for whom it was named, loved it best of all.

Where the twinflower is found there are sure to be other interesting things, like columbine, wood lily, wintergreen and bunchflower.

Lonicera involucrata, bloom

Lonicera (after Adam Lonicer) *involucrata* (flowers and fruit in an involucre). TWINBERRY HONEYSUCKLE, BEARBERRY, INVOLUCRED HONEYSUCKLE, SWAMP HONEYSUCKLE

This is the only true honeysuckle commonly found in the state. It is a shrub growing in moist, rich soil, usually near streams, at

6,000-10,000 feet elevation. It has gray stems, 2-5 feet tall, and large, opposite leaves, 2-4 inches long.

The flowers are small, yellow tubes, always in pairs, blooming in June and July. These flowers are surrounded by large, leafy involucres which turn from green to purplish-red. The fruits consist of twin, black berries about ¼ inch across, lying surrounded by the purple involucres in the fall. This is an attractive effect seen in no other plant. Flowers are visited by hummingbirds and the fruits eaten by various birds and small animals.

It can be used as an ornamental shrub, but often, under cultivation, it grows too fast and becomes coarse and scraggly. *Lonicera utahensis*, with larger flowers, fruits yellow to red, smaller bracts, and less pointed leaves, may come into the state from Utah.

(Loranthaceae **family**) on juniper

Loranthaceae family. MISTLETOE

While the mistletoes are parasitic plants and do not send their own roots into the soil, they are woody-stemmed and so should probably be classed with the shrubs. In Colorado they are occasionally seen on juniper or pine, but in some places they have become so prevalent that they seriously interfere with the normal growth of their hosts. Our species are not generally as attractive as the southern species that are used at Christmastime. The color of stems and leaves is usually a pale greenish-yellow, and the leaves are often reduced to mere scales. They are usually seen as clumps of growth on the limbs of the host tree.

The bloom is inconspicuous and the fruits are small, cream-colored, red, or orange berries filled with a sticky substance which causes them to stick to any limb on which they may fall. Birds sometimes help propagate them by carrying the berries on their feet to other limbs, where they sprout, send their roots into the host plant and feed on the host's sap.

Because mistletoe is evergreen and grows with no apparent roots high on the limbs of other trees, many legends and myths have developed about it. Some of its species are very beautiful, but generally it does much more harm than good.

Arceuthobium sp. (living on evergreens). DWARF MISTLE-TOE

This genus is found on plants other than juniper: *A. americanum* on lodgepole pine at altitudes of 8,000-10,000 feet; *A. vaginatum* (in a sheath) on ponderosa pine in the montane zone; *A. douglasii* on Douglas fir; and *A. campylopodum* (bent foot) on piñon, bristlecone or limber pine and on alpine or white fir and blue or Engelmann spruce.

Phoradendron (carrying bark). The mistletoe found on juniper and certain deciduous trees is classed in another genus: that found on juniper of the species *P. juniperinum* and on deciduous trees, *P. cockerellii.*

Lycium halimifolium. CHINESE MATRIMONY VINE

This may sometimes be found around old buildings, in ditches, and fields in the central part of the state, where it may have been brought by settlers. This shrub is sparingly-branched, spreading, or climbing, 3-15 feet tall, and spiny. Flowers are purple to light-rose and berries are salmon-red.

Lycium pallidum (pale). DESERT THORN, PALE MATRIMONY VINE, PALE WOLFBERRY (Spanish, CHICO) (see page 109)

A rare shrub of dry, rocky areas in the southwest part of the state. Has pale foliage and pale greenish-gray to dark-brown, thorny stems. Grows 2-6 feet tall and is stiff and angular looking.

The leaves are narrow, 1-2 inches long. The blooms in April and May are small, bell-shaped, greenish-purple, showing their relationship to the potato. Fruits are small, red-orange to reddish-blue berries in August. These are eaten by Indians, as well as by birds and rodents. Found frequently around ancient ruins, hence the common, local name of "Moqui bush." It is sometimes browsed by livestock.

Mamillaria **sp.,** in bloom   Mamiilaria **sp.**

Mamillaria sp. (with nipples). PINCUSHION CACTUS,
BALL CACTUS

As these have fleshy stems, persistent over the winter, they might
be classed with the shrubs. *Mamillaria* are globose or cylindrical in
shape, from 1-4 inches high, found singly or in clusters on hills or
plains in the western, southern, or central part of the state at
4,500-8,500 feet.

There are two common species: *M. missouriensis*, with yellowish-green flowers and scarlet fruit, and *M. vivipara*, with pink to
purple bloom and green fruit.

The *Mamillaria* are distinguished from other ball cactus by
being covered with small "nipples."

Menodora scabra. ROUGH MENODORA

A rare plant, reported occasionally on dry ground in the vicinity
of Pueblo and Colorado Springs. It grows 6-18 inches tall, woody
only at the base. The flowers are small, yellow, funnel-shaped; the
leaves tiny, thick, and narrow. The fruit is in twin pods, related
to the ash and forestiera.

Menziesia ferruginea (rust color). RUSTY MENZIESIA,
RUSTYLEAF

A shrub in the heath family, growing 3-6 feet tall. Common in
the Yellowstone National Park area and possibly comes into the
state from the northwest. Grows in moist, well-drained places in
the forest. Leaves have rusty-brown scales and hairs. Small, solitary, nodding flowers, globular or urn-shaped, greenish-purple in
May. Dry fruit in August. Poisonous to livestock if eaten in quantity.

119

Mimosa borealis (northern) or *fragrans*. CAT'S CLAWS (Pea family)

A small, prickly shrub growing 1½-6 feet tall, with branches often horizontal. Found on rocky hillsides and canyons in the southeastern corner of the state, at 4,000-5,000 feet. Small, compound leaves; seed pods with 1 to 7 seeds, restricted between the seeds, sometimes prickly. Small flowers with 4-5 petals and 8-10 long, pink, exserted stamens. Shrub is brittle and often broken down by overgrazing.

Opuntia **sp.**, in bloom

Opuntia sp. PRICKLY PEAR CACTUS

There are at least ten species of these with oval, flat-jointed stems, more or less creeping over the ground. The stems are fleshy rather than woody, but are persistent over the winter. They have large, beautiful, rather frail-looking flowers, mainly in pale yellows and pinks but occasionally orange or rose-purple. Most species have dry, spiny fruits but at least two have red, juicy, tasty fruits that are good to eat, when the trick of picking them is learned.

Opuntia arborescens

Opuntia arborescens, skeleton

Opuntia arborescens (tree-like) or *imbricata*. CANE CACTUS, WALKINGSTICK CHOLLA, SHRUB CACTUS, CANDELABRA CACTUS

This is a round, woody-stemmed, branched shrub growing from 3-12 feet high, occasionally on dry plains and hillsides from Colo-

120

rado Springs, south. The green stems are covered with sharp thorns and fine spines, with edges of stems comb-like. The flowers are beautiful, silky, red-purple, 2-3 inches across. The fruits, which frequently hang on all winter, are about ¾ inch across and one inch long, yellow, covered with small, spiny hairs, dry and inedible.

After a plant has been dead a few years the bark and pith of the stems fall away leaving the woody, lacework pattern of the skeleton which is used for canes and furniture.

Opuntia davisii or *whipplei*. LOW CANE CACTUS, JEFF DAVIS CHOLLA

Unlike *O. arborescens*, this species grows only 1-2 feet tall, is spreading and densely-branched, and bears yellowish flowers. The edges of the stems are not comb-like. It comes into the state occasionally from the southwest.

Oxytenia acerosa. COPPERWEED, RIGIDPLUME

A rank, quick-growing perennial, 3-6 feet high, sometimes woody at the base. The stems are slender and leafy with filiform, divided leaves. It is rush-like in appearance, sometimes leafless. The heads are numerous in dense panicles. Found in dry, alkaline areas in western Colorado at 4,500-6,500 feet. It is reported to be poisonous to stock.

Pachystima (thick stigma) *myrsinites* (like myrtle). MYRTLE BOXLEAF, MOUNTAIN LOVER (see page 153)

A low, evergreen shrub found under trees in the high mountains and mesas of the western slope. Resembles boxwood. Flowers are very small purple discs in May. Fruit dry and inconspicuous. Leaves small, leathery, dark-green, evergreen. Grows only in moist, well-drained, acid soil.

Under cultivation this would make a fine substitute for boxwood, but it will not tolerate poorly-drained alkaline soil. It is sometimes browsed by wild animals but not by domestic livestock.

Paronychia pulvinata (cushion-shaped). ROCKY MOUNTAIN NAILWORT, WHITLOW WORT

A small, cushion-like plant of alpine regions, growing 1-2 inches high. Hardly shrub-like, yet classified as such because it has a woody stem. The leaves are crowded, thick, and narrow, almost

121

moss-like. The flowers are greenish, petalless, tiny, almost hidden by the leaves.

P. jamesii, sessiliflora and *depressa* are similar but larger plants which have been found on dry plains and mesas at lower altitudes over the state.

Parryella filifolia. DUNEBROOM

A low, rush-like perennial, shrubby at the base, many-branched, growing 2-3 feet tall. The leaves are pinnately compound with small, very narrow stipulate leaflets. The flowers are small, yellowish-green, pea-like, in terminal branched spikes. The fruit is 1-seeded. Found occasionally in sandy, dry hills at about 4,500 feet in the southwestern part of the state.

Parthenocissus (virgin ivy) or *Ampelopsis vitacea, quinquifolia* (5-leaf), or *inserta.* WOODBINE, VIRGINIA CREEPER, THICKET CREEPER

A creeping or climbing vine found occasionally along streams or in moist places in the lower foothills and mesas. Probably a variety of the common Virginia creeper found over much of the United States.

Palmately 5-parted leaves which resemble poison ivy, but poison ivy has just 3 leaflets. Has no aerial rootlets or adhering discs as the eastern type has. Foliage turns a beautiful red in fall. Fruits are tiny, blue-black "grapes," eaten by many birds and some wild animals.

Peraphyllum (much leaf) *ramosissimum* (much branched). SQUAW APPLE (see page 134)

A shrub growing on dry slopes in the southwestern part of the state. Grayish bark and rigid stems, resembling flowering quince or service-berry. Covered with small, apple-like, pale-rose flowers in spring, singly or in clusters of 2 or 3 at the ends of the twigs. Fruits small, bright-red, bitter apples. Leaves dark and leathery, clustered at the ends of the twigs.

An attractive, sturdy-looking shrub, but deep-rooted and a lover of acid soil; has seldom been successfully transplanted.

122

Philadelphus microphyllus   Philadelphus microphyllus, seed heads

Philadelphus microphyllus (small leaf). LITTLELEAF MOCKORANGE

An attractive shrub of the southwestern part of the state, growing on dry slopes, 3-6 feet tall, much branched, with opposite and often vertical branches. Peeling bark, exposing several shades of brown and gray. Attractive, single, white flowers, singly or in threes, about 1½ inches across, in June and July. Small, narrow leaves, an inch or so long. There are usually some of the characteristic seed heads remaining on the bush all winter which help in identifying it.

This is probably the native mockorange that was sent to the Lemoines in France many years ago and used by them to breed hardiness into many of the modern cultivated mockoranges.

The stems were used by the Indians for arrow shafts and pipe stems.

Philadelphus nitidus and *occidentalis*, similar plants, are reported to come into the state occasionally from Utah.

Phyllodoce (a sea nymph) *empetriformis* (form of empetrum). RED MOUNTAIN HEATH, ALPINE HEATHER

A low, matted plant, under 20 inches high, found in swampy ground of the subalpine zone. An occasional specimen may have come into the state from the northwest.

Flowers rose-colored, bell-shaped, about ⅛ inch across, in heads on long stems. Leaves small, leathery, evergreen, rolled, appearing almost like fir needles.

Physocarpus bracteatus or *ramaleyi*. TWINPOD NINEBARK, RAMALEY NINEBARK

This species and *P. intermedius*, ILLINOIS NINEBARK, are occasionally found in the lower foothills, coming in from the east.

General character, bloom, and fruit are much like the cultivated ninebark, *P. opulus*. They grow 3-6 feet tall and do not sucker. There seems to be some confusion among authorities as to exact characteristics and nomenclature.

Another species, *P. malvaceus*, is reported coming into the state from Utah or Wyoming.

P. alternans has been found in Unaweep Canyon, northeast of Gateway. This has small, white, scattered flowers, 3-lobed leaves, brown stems, and grows 2-3 feet tall.

Physocarpus monogynus, in bloom   Physocarpus alternans

Physocarpus (bladder-fruit) *monogynus* (single ovary).
MOUNTAIN NINEBARK, DWARF NINEBARK, COLORADO LOW NINEBARK

A low, loose, spreading shrub found in scattered patches or covering whole hillsides, from the foothills to 9,000 feet. Always in shady places, principally on north slopes. Grows 1½-2½ feet tall and suckers freely from the roots.

Attractive flowers in small heads, resembling *Spiraea vanhouttei*. Flowers last for about 5 days in May, so entire north slopes may be white one day, and a few days later nothing will be seen. The dry seed heads turn an attractive red-brown in the fall.

Leaves are about 1½ inches long, have 3-5 lobes, and resemble a currant leaf. Bark is brown and is continually shredding off the older stems. This leaves several shades of color, the appearance that gives ninebark its name.

Sometimes used as an ornamental where its spreading, loose form is appropriate.

Physocarpus pubescens. DWARF HAIRY NINEBARK

A low (1-3 feet) spreading shrub frequenting shady places, occasionally coming into the state from Utah. Very small, round-

124

ish leaves about ⅔ inches long and shreddy, brown bark. Tiny, white flowers loosely scattered over the plant, more like snowberry than the other ninebarks. Would make a nice ornamental in places where snowberry might have been used.

Picea engelmannii. ENGELMANN SPRUCE (see page 114)
Found usually in solid stands in the subalpine zone, at 8,500-12,000 feet, all over the state, usually in association with the alpine fir. Short, square needles; smaller cones and slimmer outline than *P. pungens.* More valuable as a lumber tree than as an ornamental.

Picea pungens. COLORADO BLUE SPRUCE (see page 114)
The state tree of Colorado. Found growing along streams, generally as a specimen, at altitudes of 7,000-9,500 feet. Green to blue to silvery foliage, needles square, stiff, and sharp; large, light-brown, scaly cones of symmetrical shape. Known and used as an ornamental all over.

Pinus aristata (bristly). BRISTLECONE, FOXTAIL PINE (see page 114)
An informal tree of the subalpine area. Has long, slim limbs covered densely with needles in tufts like a bottle-brush or foxtail. The needles are medium length and in bundles of 5, indicating that it is in the white pine group. Cones are medium size with sharp bristles. It makes a nice specimen under cultivation, and although it grows naturally in a damp soil it will tolerate drought quite well. In its native habitat at timberline it often becomes quite picturesque; dead specimens are filled with pitch and weather into fantastic shapes. In recent years, ring-dating has shown some specimens of bristlecone pine to be the oldest living things in the world.

Pinus contorta latifolia. LODGEPOLE PINE (see page 114)
As found in our mountains at 6,000-11,000 feet, it is usually a tall, straight tree, crowded together with many others, with tall, bare trunks and a tuft of limbs at the top. Under cultivation it may become a nice, dense, slim tree. The cones are small and twisted, giving the tree its specific name. They may remain on the tree for several years, even becoming embedded in the wood as it grows around them. The needles are 2 in a bundle, 2-3 inches long and yellowish-green as compared with other pines. This is the tree used by the Indians for lodgepoles, giving it its common name.

Pinus edulis. PINON PINE (see page 115)

Normally grows as a small, rounded tree to 15 feet tall but may occur more like a shrub or as an even larger tree. Found in almost solid stands in places on the eastern slope and often mixed with the oneseed or desert juniper in the southwest, at 4,000 to 9,000 feet. Short, fragrant needles in clusters of 2. The cones are small and flat, producing large edible nuts which are gathered by the Indians and eaten or sold. The inner bark was also eaten by Indians in famine times. It makes a valuable tree for ornamental planting as it is rather easy to transplant and does not grow too fast. The wood is generally full of pitch and makes good firewood.

There are similar species, coming into the state from the south, which may have 3 needles in a bundle.

Pinus flexilis. LIMBER PINE (see page 115)

Found in the subalpine zone, 5,000-11,000 feet, sometimes scattered and sometimes in association with the bristlecone pine. This is also a small, informal tree with longer, slimmer needles in bundles of 5. The cones are large and pointed. The color of the foliage is often slightly bluish-green. It also makes a very valuable ornamental tree.

Pinus ponderosa. PONDEROSA PINE, ROCK PINE, JACK PINE, BULL PINE, YELLOW PINE (see page 115)

A large, massive, picturesque tree with dark-brown, coarse-ridged bark. Has large, symmetrical cones and long needles in bundles of 2 or 3. Found all over the state in hot, dry places of the plains, foothills, canyons and mesas. This is a valuable lumber tree and fills an important place as an ornamental.

Poliomintha incana (grayish-white). ROSEMARY MINT

A small shrub with felt-like tomentum, found in dry, sandy, or gypsum soil in the western or southwestern part of the state, occasionally on the desert or in canyons. It has small, linear leaves, smooth nutlets, and aromatic foliage. Bloom in axillary clusters of pale-blue, rose, or purple flowers, resembling those of mint.

Populus acuminata. LANCE-LEAF POPLAR or WYOMING COTTONWOOD

A large tree found rarely in the foothills at 4,500-8,500 feet. Intermediate in character and shape of leaf between the narrowleaf and plains cottonwoods. A similar tree called *P. andrewsii* may be a variation of this or a hybrid.

Populus angustifolia. (narrowleaf) NARROWLEAF COTTONWOOD (see page 115)
Found at 5,000-8,000 feet in canyons and along streams, generally above the range of the plains or broadleaf cottonwood. Compared with the plains cottonwood it is more upright in growth and has smoother, whiter, upper limbs. The leaves are so narrow that they are often mistaken for those of willow.

Populus balsamifera. BALSAM POPLAR
Leaves ovate-lanceolate, dark-green above and whitish below. Groves found rarely in the central or north-central part of the state at 6,000-12,000 feet. Buds are fragrant and waxy. Intermediate in character between the narrowleaf cottonwood and the quaking aspen.

Populus sargentii. PLAINS COTTONWOOD (see page 115)
A large, spreading tree with deeply-furrowed bark on the older trunks, and broad-bladed leaves. Found on the eastern plains and up in the foothills from 3,500-6,500 feet. Always found where there is some moisture in the soil. Where there is room for its great size, it makes a good ornamental shade tree, much hardier than the Carolina poplar imported from the east. By planting only trees grown from cuttings of male trees, the objectionable "cotton" flying everywhere in the spring may be eliminated.

Populus tremuloides. QUAKING ASPEN (see page 112)
Usually a small tree but under favorable soil and moisture conditions it may become large. Conspicuous for its smooth white bark (or brownish-white on less vigorous trees). Often seen in large groves, sometimes covering whole mountainsides, but may be scattered among other trees anywhere there is moisture in the soil. Found at 6,000-10,000 feet. The bloom is in catkins, the staminate and pistillate on separate trees. The fruit is in cottony masses. The wood has been used for matchsticks, excelsior, or crating. Can be grown as an ornamental at lower altitudes if carefully transplanted and kept free of scale insects. This tree is the main source of fall color in the mountains; whole hillsides become masses of golden-yellow around the first of October.

Populus wislizeni. RIO GRANDE POPLAR

Similar to the plains cottonwood in size and general character, but has leaves with coarser teeth and grows in the southwestern part of the state on the plains and canyons at 4,000-7,000 feet.

Potentilla fruticosa, in bloom

Potentilla (powerful) or *Dasiophora fruticosa* (shrubby). BUSH CINQUEFOIL, SHRUBBY CINQUEFOIL

Found usually in open areas in moist ground, but occasionally in dry, shady, or other unlikely places throughout the state. This and an alpine currant probably grow at a higher altitude than any other woody plant. Normally grows 1-3 feet tall but above timberline may be a very low, mat plant. Sometimes the plants are well shaped and compact but are often scraggly from grazing.

It may be identified all summer by the small, yellow, rose-like bloom and all winter by the persistent, brown fruit heads and brown, shreddy bark. The grayish-green, hairy leaves are usually palmately 5-parted (cinquefoil) but sometimes they may have 3 or 7 divisions. Browsed some by wild and domestic animals. Easily transplanted and makes a nice ornamental shrub. Many cultivated and named varieties have been developed from this.

Prosopis glandulosa (full of glands), *juliflora*, or *chilensis.*
HONEY MESQUITE

A common, large shrub or small tree along watercourses or on overgrazed land below 6,000 feet, coming occasionally into the state from New Mexico. Much-branched in a zig-zag manner, somewhat like a dwarf honey locust. Sometimes forms a large, woody stem above ground or may be covered several feet deep with drift sand. Roots are reported to penetrate 50 feet or more in search of water. It is very hardy and aggressive.

Bears fragrant, creamy-yellow spikes of small flowers in April or later, which are very attractive to bees. The fruits are sweet-meated pods, 4-8 inches long, compressed between seeds. This is an important source of food for wild animals, birds, and some Indians. Leaves are compound, with more than 9 pairs of leaflets. The plant bears stout, yellowish spines.

The inner bark was used by the Indians for cordage or baskets. The tree is often host to the parasitic mistletoe.

Prunus americana   Prunus americana, bloom

Prunus americana. AMERICAN PLUM, WILD PLUM

Found in dense, almost impenetrable thickets along stream-sides and moist places in the eastern foothills and out on the plains. Usually seen as a dense, thorny mass about 6-8 feet tall but occasional specimens may become 10-12 feet tall.

Very attractive in May when covered with the rather large, white flowers. The fruit is ¾ to 1 inch in diameter and usually red when ripe. It may vary considerably in character and taste, but is used quite commonly for jam and canning. It is rather sweet at first taste but has a bitter area near the seed. There is a disease which sometimes attacks the plum after blooming that absorbs the seed and inflates the skin to several times normal size, with a peculiar "mouldy" color. The general appearance of a clump of wild plum is gray but the older trunks are darker. It is sometimes used for ornamental thickets or "jungle" screens.

Prunus besseyi. WESTERN SAND CHERRY

A low, spreading shrub, seldom over 3 feet tall. Occasionally found on the plains and into the foothills of the northeastern part of the state where soil and moisture conditions are favorable. The species *P. pumila,* EASTERN SAND CHERRY, is often confused with this, but is taller and more erect in habit.

129

The flowers in May are good-sized, white, and attractive. The fruits are ½-¾ inches in diameter, plum-shaped, blue-black but sometimes reddish. They are edible but usually have a peculiar bitter taste. Strains have been developed from better specimens which are useful for fruit as well as for ornament.

Prunus pennsylvanica, bloom   Prunus pennsylvanica, fruit

Prunus pennsylvanica or *saximontana*. PIN CHERRY, BIRD CHERRY, WILD RED CHERRY

A very attractive tall shrub or small tree found occasionally from the foothills to 9,500 feet through the central part of the state. Most often seen as scattered specimens under trees but sometimes grows on hillsides, where it is seldom over 4 feet tall. Spreads from shallow roots, but usually found in scattered clumps rather than in the dense masses of the chokecherry or plum.

The bark is smooth, brown, and spotted much like the familiar cultivated cherry, and the bloom is white, in small flat heads, in May, like the domestic cherry. Very attractive when in bloom; this is the time to locate it, for it is rather inconspicuous at other times.

The fruits are also very attractive, consisting of clusters of bright-red cherries about ¼ inch in diameter. These are little more than a skin stretched over a large seed, but birds seem to prefer them to cultivated cherries. The leaves are attractive, long-pointed, with saw-toothed edges.

May be used as a tall, ornamental shrub where its spreading habit and short life are not objectionable.

Prunus virginiana demissa, bloom   Prunus virginiana demissa, fruit

Prunus virginiana demissa or *melanocarpa*. WESTERN
CHOKECHERRY

A very common, tall shrub along streams and on hillsides from
the plains to 9,000 feet or more. In moist places it grows 8-15
feet tall, often forming dense thickets, but on dry hillsides it grows
as a spreading shrub 3-4 feet tall. Occasionally, in rich soil and
under heavy grazing conditions, it may become tree-like with a
trunk 3-4 inches in diameter.

This is one of our very attractive shrubs when in bloom. The
flowers are small, white, and arranged in finger-like pendant clusters 3-6 inches long. The blooming season varies from April to
June depending on the altitude. The flowers are attractively
fragrant. Clusters of fruit ⅓-½ inch in diameter follow the flowers. These are first green, then red, and finally black when ripe.

The plant is readily identified, winter or summer, by the light
spots (lenticels) on the dark bark and by the almond taste when
a twig is chewed.

Indians used to camp near big stands of chokecherries; the
squaws would gather them, pound them up, seed and all, and mix
them, dried, into their concentrated pemmican. Indians also made
a red dye from the berries and a green dye from the bark. The
berries are relished by many birds and other wildlife, especially
bears. They are a little too puckery to be eaten raw by humans,
but make excellent jelly and jam when mixed with apples or other
fruit. The plant makes a valuable ornamental shrub where a tall,
hardy spreading plant is needed.

Some authors list *P. demissa* and *P. melanocarpa* as separate
species, rather than varieties, but the distinction is rather vague.

131

Pseudotsuga (like a hemlock) *taxifolia* (yew-like foliage).
DOUGLAS FIR (see page 114)

Found all over the state at much the same altitude as the ponderosa pine but in solid stands on the north slopes or in shady places. Somewhat similar to spruce in appearance but softer and more informal. The needles are about the same length as those of spruce but blunt, flat, and soft. Cones are dark brown, pendant, persistent, having three-pronged bracts between the scales. It is an alternate host of the spruce gall aphid and so is not usually planted as an ornamental close to spruce.

Ptelea baldwinii

Ptelea baldwinii, crenulata, or *angustifolia*. HOPTREE, WAFER ASH

A large shrub found occasionally in south-central Colorado, notably along the Arkansas River above Canon City. Flowers small, greenish-white, in April or May. Fruits consist of drooping clusters of winged seeds, about ¾ inch across, resembling hops. These often hang on all winter and help to identify the plant. Leaves 3-parted, leaflets 1-3 inches long, aromatic when bruised, dark-green above, paler and dotted below.

This plant has some medicinal properties and was used by the Indians for many things.

There seems to be some confusion among botanists as to the extent and characters of species, but the plant found wild in Colorado usually differs from the cultivated hoptree by being shorter and by having narrower leaflets and slimmer stems.

Purshia tridentata (3-toothed leaf). ANTELOPE-BRUSH, BITTERBRUSH

Found only occasionally in some areas but as the principal shrub in other areas; growing in dry, rocky places in the ponderosa pine zone, from 6,000-9,000 feet, scattered over much of the state. It forms a low, spreading, irregularly-branched shrub 2-4 feet high.

Blooms are very attractive in May, about ½ inch across, light-yellow, and pleasantly fragrant. They are arranged on artistically arched stems, often one stem blooming before the others. Fruits are small, pointed pods from the old flower heads; these are intensely bitter if chewed. Leaves are less than an inch long, narrow, wedge-shaped, 3-toothed at the apex, clustered on the ends of the twigs, white-hairy beneath and darker above, turning yellowish with drought. The bark is brownish-gray and the general effect of the shrub, when not in bloom, is that of a desert plant.

In some areas it forms an important source of browse for game animals and domestic stock, except horses. It would make a good cultivated ornamental, but being a plant of dry, well-drained places it is not easily transplanted and does not tolerate overwatering in the summer.

Quercus gambelii,   Quercus turbinella   Quercus **sp.**, bloom

Quercus gambelii. GAMBEL OAK, SCRUB OAK

Scrub oaks occur in Colorado largely in the southern and western parts, coming north to Denver on the eastern slope and to Steamboat Springs on the western slope. They are variable in size, running all the way from matted shrubs 4-8 feet high to small trees with a trunk diameter of 6-8 inches. The bloom of oaks comes very early, just as the leaves are starting, and so are seldom noticed. The staminate bloom consists of long tassels of tiny, greenish-yellow flowers which soon drop off; then the still less conspicuous pistillate bloom develops, which later forms the acorns.

133

Peraphyllum ramosissimum (p. 122)

Peraphyllum ramosissimum (p. 122)

Rhamnus betulaefolia (p. 137)

Rhamnus smithii (p. 137)

ibes wolfii (p. 144)

Ribes setosum (p. 144)

Ribes montigenum (p. 144)

Robinia neomexicana (p. 145)

Ribes montigenum (p. 144)

Ribes montigenum (p. 144)

The leaves are almost all typical of the white oak group, with rounded lobes, but variable as to size, depth of lobes, and number of lobes. Acorns also vary in size and in the proportion of the nut covered by the cap. This variableness has caused various authorities to name many species and subspecies, but the gradation of one to another is often so slight that the tendency now is to lump most species found in the state together under the name *Quercus gambelii.*

Oaks are difficult to transplant. The acorns are also difficult to collect or sprout; either rodents gather them as soon as ripe, or they seem to contain the larvae of a worm which soon eats out the germ. Most acorns have a bitter taste from the tannic acid contained, but all are nourishing and can be treated by leaching or boiling to make them palatable. Sometimes they may be quite sweet and tasty.

Quercus gunnisonii. GUNNISON OAK

Generally found in the southern part of the state. It is usually a low shrub and is supposed to have distinctive leaf and acorn characteristics. Usually it is classed as a variety of *Q. gambelii.*

Quercus leptophylla. SOCCORRO OAK or ROCKY MOUNTAIN WHITE OAK

Generally a small tree, found occasionally in the southern and western part of the state.

Quercus novomexicana. NEW MEXICAN SHINNERY OAK

One common subspecies found in the southern part of the state.

Quercus turbinella (top-shaped) CALIFORNIA SCRUB OAK or EVERGREEN LIVE OAK

A compact shrub, 3-8 feet tall. The leaves are distinctive in being evergreen, twisted, and spiny, similar to holly. It is rare in the southwestern corner of the state, growing in cracks of rocks on rocky mesas.

Quercus undulata. DESERT OAK, WAVYLEAF OAK

A small shrub that comes into the state from the southwest and is found occasionally as far east and north as Canon City. It is distinctive enough to warrant a separate species. In southwestern desert locations it is usually only a foot or so high, growing in dense masses from underground runners. These clumps often collect blowing sand until they become mounds as much as 6 feet high. *Q. undulata pungens* is supposed to be a type of this oak, with leaves more twisted.

Quercus utahensis, or *submollis*. UTAH WHITE OAK
Usually a very large shrub or small tree, coming into the state from Utah and appearing occasionally as far east as Palmer Lake. Now usually classed as a variety of *Q. gambelii*.

Quercus vreelandii, VREELAND OAK
Generally a smaller shrub found over the southern half of the state.

Rhamnus betulaefolia (birch leaf). BIRCHLEAF BUCKTHORN (see page 134)
This species has wider, birch-like, deeply-veined leaves which are rather attractive. It may come into the state from Utah, along streams.
The buckthorns were used as medicine by primitive Indians and later by the settlers. The bark furnishes cascara, used as a tonic.

Rhamnus smithii. SMITH BUCKTHORN, ALGERITA-BERRY (see page 134)
An attractive, large, leafy shrub, occasionally found growing in moist places in the southwestern quarter of the state. Generally appears as a symmetrical specimen much like chokecherry or willow. Flowers small and greenish in May or June. Fruit a black berry about ½ inch long, in October. Leaves 1-2 inches long, about 3 times as long as wide, glossy above, appearing almost opposite.
Should make a good ornamental shrub.

Rhododendron albiflorum, leaf, bloom, habitat

Rhododendron or *Azaleastrum albiflorum* (white flower).
WHITE-FLOWERED AZALEA, CASCADE FALSE
AZALEA

So far as is known, this shrub is found in the state only on the upper slopes of streams in the vicinity of Ethel Peak and Mt. Zirkel, north of Steamboat Springs. It grows singly or matted together on steep hillside "swamps" where the soil is largely peat and constantly wet, under trees or in the open, almost to timberline. It grows 3-5 feet high and is usually rather well-shaped. The blooms consist of flat, white flowers about as large as a quarter, opening in July. They are not free-flowering and are seldom seen in full bloom. The fruits are dry and inconspicuous. The leaves are small, slightly twisted, yellowish-green and appear somewhat chlorotic. They resemble closely the leaves of the florists' azaleas.

This isolated stand of rhododendrons may be a leftover from the early times when climate all over the area was more favorable to many plants now found only in more moist areas. Apparently the closest place where this species now grows is in Oregon. It may furnish valuable breeding stock from which a hardy rhododendron for the Denver area might be grown. It is very unlikely that any specimens moved to drier climates would survive.

Rhus glabra, leaves   Rhus glabra, fruit

Rhus glabra or *cismontana*. ROCKY MOUNTAIN
SMOOTH SUMAC

A dwarf form of the eastern smooth sumac, growing in well-drained, sunny places, usually in solid masses but sometimes singly. Found throughout the southeastern foothills or in the southwest. It has large, single or branched stems, 2-5 feet tall, depending on soil and moisture. There are 9-17 leaflets, similar to the familiar cultivated species. These turn a brilliant red in fall, coloring whole hillsides in places. The red berries, borne in pointed heads, are slightly acid and edible; they make a substitute for lemonade. Indians made a dye from the roots. The leaves and bark contain tannic acid. Indians and later inhabitants used parts of the plant medicinally.

This is a neat ornamental for hot, dry places where a light shrub is needed. For many spots it is more valuable than the larger, eastern kinds because it remains a lower growth. It is easily transplanted, as it is shallow-rooted.

Rhus radicans, fruit   Rhus radicans, leaves

Rhus radicans or *toxicodendron*, or *Toxicodendron rydbergii*.

WESTERN POISON IVY (Spanish, YEDRA)

Found largely in the foothills area, in moist places along the base of hills, by streams and at the edge of forests. It is usually 6-18 inches high, but sometimes grows up to 3-4 feet tall in the southwest. The stems are erect and covered with large, 3-parted leaves. It is similar in appearance to Engelmann ivy, which has 5 leaflets. It does not climb or vine in this area.

The leaves turn an attractive red in fall and in winter the short stems bear clusters of creamy-white berries, eaten by some birds with no apparent bad effect. Both the nice leaves and berries have caused many not familiar with the plant to pick it for decoration, to their sorrow. Some people are much more susceptible to the poison than others, but in general it is much easier to be poisoned when sweaty than when cool. A good rule is to completely wash hands, face and neck after being near poison ivy. Clear water will help if used quickly and washing with soapy water will usually remove all poison before it takes hold, if it is done within a few minutes. It is a good practice for all who walk through foothills country to learn this plant and avoid it. Remember that it has 3 leaflets rather than 5.

139

Rhus trilobata   Rhus trilobata, fruit   Rhus trilobata, bloom

Rhus trilobata (3-lobed). SKUNKBRUSH SUMAC,
THREELEAF SUMAC, LEMONADE SUMAC, SQUAWBUSH,
SKUNKBRUSH (Spanish, LEMITA)

Growing all over the state in the driest places on the plains, foothills, mesas and desert, at low altitudes below 8,000 feet. This is a branched shrub, 2-8 feet high, sometimes seen as a well-formed specimen and often in dense "jungles." Leaves rarely entire, usually 3-parted but sometimes merely 3-lobed. They are about 1-1½ inches across, dark-green above. Always identifiable, winter or summer, by the rank, skunky odor of the stems when bruised.

The bloom is of tiny, yellow flowers in small clusters, appearing even before the leaves. The fruits are clusters of red berries. These are covered with sticky glands which, in time, collect webs and dust and look untidy. They are really quite interesting because they produce an acid similar to that of lemon. A few rolled under the tongue (not chewed) for half a minute will give a refreshing acid taste like chewing lemon, and a handful of them stirred in a glass of water with a little sugar makes a drink hardly distinguishable from lemonade. The fruits are also eaten by many kinds of birds and game and were eaten raw or dried by the Indians. The stems are used in Indian basketry.

It makes an attractive, cultivated shrub for dry, difficult conditions.

Rhus trilobata simplicifolia is a similar plant with simple leaves occasionally found in the southwestern part of the state. Since all gradations of leaf form are found this is probably not a separate species.

140

Ribes **sp.,** bloom

Ribes leptanthum, fruit

Ribes cereum, bloom

Ribes cereum, fruit

Ribes cereum

Ribes coloradense, bloom

Ribes americanum. AMERICAN BLACK CURRANT

Found occasionally in damp, shady woods and along the lower streams in the eastern foothills. It is usually a cluster of straight or arching stems, 2-4 feet high, much resembling the cultivated currant.

Leaves 1½-2½ inches broad, sharply 3- 5-lobed, veined beneath, maple-like. Flowers small and greenish, in April or May. Berries black, about ¼ inch in diameter, round, puckery, in clusters.

Ribes aureum (yellow) or *longiflorum.* GOLDEN CURRANT, BUFFALO CURRANT

Found along streams and in open places in the plains and foothills all over the state. Grows as a thin shrub or in well-formed clumps, with stems 2-6 feet tall, straight, arching, or branched. Stems smooth; leaves smooth, 3-lobed, wedge-shaped. Flowers yellow, tube-shaped, ¾ to 1 inch long, fragrant, and full of nectar; some like to eat them. Fruit about ¼ inch in diameter, round, juicy, not very acid, black or yellow.

A very valuable shrub for wild or roadside planting and for coarse screens. It spreads by underground suckers and will grow in dry places where few other plants will survive. Berries much loved by birds, and make good jam.

There seems to be a distinct type that grows along the Green River and other rivers in the western part of the state which grows up to 12 feet tall, with glossy, rounded leaves.

Ribes cereum (wax) or *inebrians.* WAX CURRANT, SQUAW CURRANT

Found on dry, sunny slopes throughout the foothills, into the montane and touching the subalpine zones. Generally associated with the ponderosa pine and seen as a well-shaped, specimen shrub. Stems smooth, branched, with almost cherry-like bark. Leaves roundish, 1½ inches broad, with distinctive odor, fuzzy and sticky. Flowers hanging, pinkish, tubular, about ⅓ inch long in June. Fruit red, smooth when ripe in August. Eaten by birds and by humans when there is rain enough before ripening to fill the berries out. Before eating them the dried flower must be pinched off to avoid a bad-tasting pitchy flavor. Slightly poisonous if eaten in quantity, but used by the Hopi Indians as a cure for stomachache.

Because of its habit of growth and color of fruit, this shrub is distinct from other native currants. Useful as a cultivated ornamental, but is often subject to a disease which makes the leaves pale and chlorotic. Very similar to the cultivated alpine currant, but inferior under cultivation.

Ribes viscosissimum (sticky) is a similar shrub with larger leaves and ranker growth occasionally found in the northwestern corner of the state.

Ribes coloradense. SUBALPINE BLACK CURRANT, COLORADO CURRANT

A rambling, procumbent, spineless shrub of well-drained subalpine areas, largely on the western slope. Large heart- or kidney-shaped leaves, 1¼-2 inches broad, smooth, 5-lobed, resembling maple leaves, mainly on the ends of the stems. Brown bark, twigs hairy and sticky. Round, black fruit, with "bloom," glandular and sticky, not very tasty, but eaten by wild birds and animals. Pinkish or purplish saucer-shaped flowers, springing in clusters from the previous year's wood.

Ribes inerme (unarmed) or *saxosum.* WHITESTEM GOOSEBERRY

The common gooseberry of moist places in the foothills up through the montane zone. Usually under 3 feet high, with long, pale, arching stems. May have a few short spines at the nodes and some short bristles between, or may be almost spineless. Smooth leaves, 3- 5-lobed, about 1 inch long. Flowers 2-4 in a cluster, greenish or pinkish, tubular or bell-shaped, in June. Fruit large, black, ¼ inch i ndiameter, smooth, tart, but edible raw, and adding wonderful flavor to jams when mixed with apples and other fruit. Makes an attractive high ground cover under cultivation, which is not easily trampled by boys or dogs.

Ribes lacustre (of lakes) or *parvulum.* SMALL-FRUITED GOOSEBERRY

A procumbent shrub of the montane zone, mainly on the western slope. Found on dry hillsides and timbered slopes. Spines weak, single at the nodes, and bristly between them. Small leaves, ¾ to 1¼ inch, 3- 5-lobed, smooth. Green-to-purplish, saucer-shaped bloom. Small, black, bristly fruit, not tasty.

Ribes leptanthum (slender). TRUMPET GOOSEBERRY

A branched and rigid shrub, 1½-6 feet high, coming into the state in sunny places, from the south and west. Leaves very small, ½ inch long, deeply-obed, smooth, roundish. Usually single, long spines at the nodes; young shoots very spiny and old shoots smooth. Flowers in April small, yellowish, bell-shaped; calyx hairy. Makes a nice, rounded shrub for ornamental use, but is a little particular about having good drainage.

Ribes montigenum (of mountains) or *lentum*. RED-FRUITED GOOSEBERRY, MOUNTAIN GOOSEBERRY (see page 135)

A small, spiny shrub found in wet forests and along streams in the subalpine and alpine zones. Leaves less than 1 inch wide, 5-lobed, hairy, and glandular. Flowers purplish or greenish, tube- or saucer-shaped. Small, red fruit, glandular or bristly, not especially tasty. Spines 3 to a node.

Ribes setosum (bristly) or *saximontanum*. REDSHOOT GOOSEBERRY, ROCKY MOUNTAIN GOOSEBERRY (see page 135)

Found rarely in the montane zone and below, in much the same range as *R. inerme*. Similar in general habit and size. Leaves more deeply-lobed than those of *R. inerme* and slightly hairy. Flowers 2-4 in a cluster, tubular or bell-shaped, white tinged with violet. Fruit reddish-purple, acid, and good for jam. Long, sharp spines, usually 2-3 at the nodes.

Ribes wolfii. WOLF'S CURRANT, ROTHROCK CURRANT (see page 135)

A loose, erect shrub found from the upper montane zone to slightly above timberline, often in partial shade. Leaves large, 1¼-2½ inches, 3- 5-lobed, smooth above, thickish, pale, and hairy underneath, and mainly at the ends of the bare stems. May grow 2-4 feet tall in moist woods. Very similar to *R. coloradense*. Flowers small, yellowish-white to red, bell-shaped, terminal on current year's growth. Young branches glandular-pubescent. Fruit round, black with "bloom," ¼ inch in diameter, sticky-bristly when young, becoming smooth when ripe. Dry and insipid but eaten by birds.

Robinia neomexicana. NEW MEXICAN LOCUST, PINK LOCUST, SOUTHWESTERN LOCUST (see page 135)

A tall shrub or small tree which can grow up to 25 feet high, but generally reaches 6-10 feet. Found in the southern part of the state in the lower foothills, conspicuously on Raton Pass.

The leaves are compound, similar to those of the familiar black locust. Stems are covered with simple thorns. The flowers are like hanging clusters of pink sweet peas. With age the plant grows sparse and scraggly, but a young specimen covered with bloom is a beautiful sight. The fruits are hairy pods, 3-4 inches long.

Sometimes planted as an ornamental where its size and spreading habit are not objectionable. Because it spreads by underground suckers, it is a valuable plant for erosion control, but it is not immune to attacks by the damaging locust borer. It was used by the Indians as a medicine and is sometimes eaten by stock (especially the bloom), but it has the reputation of being slightly poisonous. A prick from the thorns feels like a bee sting.

Rosa sp. WILD ROSE   Rosa **sp.**

It is easy to identify the wild roses because of their familiar compound foliage, attractive, single, pink to white flowers and bright red fruits. It is more difficult to distinguish between the species, because they evidently hybridize easily and there are many gradations between the recognizable species. They are found all over the state in all kinds of places, sometimes forming dense mats or thickets because of their suckering habit. Some never grow over a foot high while others may attain 4 feet or more.

Some have darker petals than others and the size of the flowers varies from 1-2 inches across. The bloom is mainly in June and most flowers have a pleasant fragrance. The fruits (hips or apples) are also quite variable, some being small, hard, round balls with a mealy pulp covering a few bony seeds, while others may be pear-shaped and quite juicy. These fruits hang on late and may be eaten by many kinds of birds and animals. They make pleasant eating for humans, especially as a mild jelly. The petals may also be eaten or dried for perfume. The Indians used the fruit and petals in many ways as medicine. One interesting remedy was to mix the dried petals with wildcat fat as a treatment for eczema. The fruits, very rich in vitamins, have been gathered extensively for use as a vitamin supplement.

All species are adaptable to cultivated use where the suckering habit is not objectionable. Some kinds have attractive red bark and persistent red fruit and provide good winter color. The form and fragrance of wild roses have made them the favorite flowers of many.

At least 5 species are generally recognized, though some writers list many more:

Rosa arkansana. ARKANSAS ROSE
Found in eastern Colorado and the southwestern corner at lower altitudes. It grows 6-24 inches high. Stems have bristles but not large prickles and are sometimes winterkilled to the ground. There are usually several flowers in a cluster.

Rosa acicularis (prickly). PRICKLY ROSE
Found generally over the state except in the northern part. Flowers are large and 1-3 on a stem. Stems are hardy and have bristles but no large prickles.

Rosa woodsii or *fendleri.*
Found all over the state at altitudes of 3,500-9,000 feet. The flowers are small and many, from new branches. The stems have both bristles and large prickles, and they may grow 3-8 feet high.

Rosa nutkana or macdougalii.
This grows generally over the state, becoming 3 feet tall or more. It is hardy and much-branched, bearing spines, but with bristles only at the base. Flowers are 1-3 on a stem, and the fruits are often spiny.

Rosa engelmannii.
Found in the west-central part of the state at altitudes of 8,000-10,000 feet. Flowers are solitary or few on a stem. Stems are hardy and have both bristles and spines.

Rubus deliciosus

Rubus parviflorus

Rubus strigosus, bloom

Rubus strigosus, leaves

Rubus strigosus, fruit

Rubus deliciosus or *Bossekia deliciosa*. THIMBLEBERRY,
BOULDER RASPBERRY

Probably our most attractive native shrub, resembling somewhat
the bridal wreath spirea in habit, size, gracefulness of growth and
ease of transplanting. Grows in rocky places all through the mountains and foothills, usually as a specimen plant. Attractive leaves,
1-2 inches across, lobed and toothed. Flowers like large, white,
single roses, about 1½ inches across and usually set singly on
short stems. Fruits are large, flat, purplish, and have a peculiar
flavor which is not appreciated at first, but which some people
learn to like. They cannot be picked when ripe, as they fall to
pieces, but must be individually sucked from the stems. Eaten by
birds and animals.

This shrub does well under cultivation if not overwatered in the
summer and fall. Its effect, when planted along a highway in the
mountains, is most nearly like that of the flowering dogwood of
the South and East.

Rubus parviflorus (few-flowered). SALMONBERRY, WHITE-
FLOWERING RASPBERRY, WESTERN THIMBLEBERRY

This is found in moist places in the montane and subalpine
zones on the western slope. The stems are few, simple and erect,
2-3 feet high, with shreddy bark, probably biennial. Large (1½
inch) white flowers in clusters of 2-4, opening one at a time. The
fruit is red, large, but rather dry and tasteless and falls apart when
picked. The leaves are few but very large, 4-8 inches, deeply-lobed
and quite attractive. The fruit is eaten by wild birds and animals.
The leaves have been used for tea and the young shoots for greens.

It is attractive in a wild garden where the suckering habit is not
objectionable.

Rubus strigosus (with furrows) or *idaeus*. WILD RED
RASPBERRY, AMERICAN RED RASPBERRY

Found growing in loose soil and on open slopes from the foothills to subalpine areas. Stems 1-2 feet high, very prickly, probably
biennial. Leaves compound, flowers white and inconspicuous.

The fruit is probably the tastiest of all Colorado native fruits.
It is wonderful when eaten right from the plant and makes good
jelly and jam, but the berries are very fragile and will not stand
much handling. It is easy to transplant and will add much to a wild

garden. It grows especially vigorously on new highway grades and burned-over areas, which gives a clue to some of its best uses.

Other species which might occasionally be seen:

Rubus exrubicundus.

Has large white flowers, small leaves and small, dry fruit. Upright, smooth stems, 3-4 feet high. Possibly coming into the state from New Mexico, at 5,000-6,000 feet.

Rubus occidentalis. BLACKCAP RASPBERRY

Prickly, arching stems, rooting at the tips. Black fruit and white flowers. Found occasionally in the north-central part of state at about 5,500 feet. May have escaped cultivation.

Rubus ?? TRAILING RASPBERRY

This delicate little vine is occasionally found growing with other small plants in remote, moist spots of the mountains, notably along small streams in the Devil's Head Mountain area, southwest of Denver. Flowers are tiny on upright stems with the white petals barely showing. Fruit small and dry. Not listed by most botanists. Makes a fine rock garden plant.

Salix anglorum antiplasta

Salix pseudolapponum, habitat

Salix **sp.**, with "pussies"

149

Large shrub Salix, "pussies"

Shrub Salix, "pussies"

Salix exigua, foliage

Salix exigua, "pussies"

Salix anglorum antiplasta or *S. petrophila* or *S. arctica petraea*.
SKYLAND WILLOW, ROCK WILLOW,
ALPINE WILLOW

A tiny, creeping mat-plant found above timberline. Grows 2-4 inches high with small, round, dark-green, shiny leaves, pale underneath. Hardly recognizable as a willow until the familiar catkin bloom appears in spring; also, there are small, gnarled, woody stems from which the new growth comes each year. This species has yellow petioles and twigs, and longer leaves than other alpine species.

Salix cascadensis. CASCADES WILLOW

A rare species, similar to skyland willow, with leaves light-green on both surfaces. Found on Trail Ridge.

Salix nivalis (showy). SNOW WILLOW

The tiniest of all alpine willows. Similar to skyland willow but not as common or at least not as noticeable. Leaves glaucous beneath.

Salix saximontana or *reticulata*. SUMMIT WILLOW

A low mat-plant, common above timberline. Round leaves. Similar to skyland or snow willow and possibly a variation in form or nomenclature. Generally larger and more common.

Salix brachycarpa (short-fruited) BARRENGROUND
WILLOW

Primarily a subalpine willow but occasionally found above timberline. Common in wet places, forming thickets. Usually less than 3 feet high; stems reddish-brown to yellowish or gray. Twigs silky-hairy, grayish-yellow. Leaves oblong, light-green and tomentose above, yellowish-green and densely tomentose beneath.

Salix pseudolapponum or *glaucops*. SUBALPINE WILLOW

Found in boggy places just above and below timberline. May grow 1½ to 5 feet high. Stems prostrate, first brown and shiny and later dull-gray. Leaves grayish overall; darker above, netted below, petioles yellowish.

Salix nelsonii, NELSON'S WILLOW, and *Salix planifolia monica*, PLANELEAF WILLOW are other subalpine willows or variations of the above. *Salix planifolia or chlorophylla* is a small shrub about 2 feet tall which may be found in montane and subalpine areas. *S. glauca, S. cordifolia* and *S. candida* are small shrubs under 2 feet high found only in Rocky Mountain National Park or nearby.

Salix monticola or *S. pseudomonticola padophylla*. MOUNTAIN WILLOW

The most common tall willow of the subalpine or montane zones, growing 3-12 feet tall. Twigs stout and lustrous, reddish-brown to a striking yellow. Leaves dark above and glaucous beneath, gray on both sides.

A similar but smaller species, *S. pseudomonticola*, may be found rarely over the state at much the same altitude.

Salix wolfii. WOLF'S WILLOW

Similar to mountain willow but only 2-3 feet high. *S. barclayi*, a similar species 6-8 feet high, is found on the northern part of the front range at 7,000-10,000 feet.

Salix bebbiana or *rostrata*. BEBB WILLOW, BEAKED WILLOW

A common willow along streambanks and lake shores from the foothills to the subalpine zone. Grows almost tree-like at times, but is usually a shrub 6-15 feet high. Twigs slender, spreading, full of leaf scars. Very small leaves, dull-green above and paler and netted on under side, pubescent top and bottom. Similar to *S. geyeriana* but no "bloom" on twigs.

The shrub willows often furnish the only food and building material for beavers when aspen are not available. The buds are also eaten by deer and grouse. All willows are distinguished from the poplars by having just one bud scale that covers the bud like a little hood.

Salix scouleriana, nuttallii or *flavescens*. SCOULER WILLOW

A tall (6-12 feet) sometimes tree-like willow, common from the foothills to the subalpine zone. Generally found along mountain streams but sometimes occurs on apparently dry ground. Bark gray; slender dark-yellow twigs; leaves large, dark-green and tomentose above, glaucous and veined beneath. Conspicuous for the large oval catkins, especially in May when they are yellow with pollen.

152

Salix irrorata (p. 155)

Salix amygdaloides (p. 154)

Tamarix gallica (p. 166)

Pachystima myrsinites (p. 121)

Salix caudata or *fendleriana*. WHIPLASH WILLOW

A shrub willow common from the foothills to the subalpine zone. Generally seen as a dense shrub, 5-10 feet high. Conspicuous for its stout, shiny, yellowish or reddish twigs which make masses of interesting color along many mountain streams and pastures. Also attractive when the seed pods burst, spilling out millions of "cotton" balls. Leaves narrow, smooth, dark-green above and paler beneath, margins glandular-serrate.

There is reported a similar species, *S. serissima*, AUTUMN WILLOW, rarely in Boulder County, and *S. lucida* rarely in extreme eastern Colorado.

Salix amygdaloides. PEACHLEAF WILLOW (see page 153)

Generally a small tree with one or several stems, growing 15-30 feet high. Has dark, ridged bark on the main trunks. Found mainly on the eastern plains from 3,500-7,500 feet, along streams and wherever there is moist ground. Almost the only thing, other than windmills, to break the skyline in many areas.

Salix lasiandra (wooly). PACIFIC WILLOW

Small trees with stout branches. Leaves lanceolate, dark-green and shiny above, glaucous beneath, glandular, serrate. Found occasionally in the southwestern corner of the state, along streams and moist meadows.

Salix lutea. YELLOW WILLOW

Small trees or shrubs. Twigs yellow, red on one side. Rare at 7,000-8,000 feet on eastern or western slopes.

Salix exigua. SANDBAR or COYOTE WILLOW (Spanish, JARITA)

This willow is common over the state, along streams and moist washes, usually at lower altitudes on the plains, over the desert, and into the foothills. The leaves are distinctively narrow, white-hairy below. Slender, erect, gray to red-brown stems, 6-15 feet tall, matted together where conditions are favorable. Interesting when in bloom or fruit. A creek bed lined with these willows gives a gray-brown effect.

The Indians used the long, flexible stems of this and other willows for weaving baskets.

Other similar species or synonymous names are *S. exigua*

luteosericea; S. exigua stenophylla and *S. interior.* One similar species, *S. melanopsis tenerrima,* smaller and with red stems, has been found in Jackson County.

Sometimes these may be found in drier areas or at higher altitudes.

Salix irrorata. BLUESTEM WILLOW (see page 153)

This conspicuous native shrub willow has distinctive "blue" stems from the previous year's growth. This whitish "bloom" will rub off, leaving the twigs red or dark gray. Grows along streams in the foothills of the eastern slope, from 5,000-7,000 feet. May grow 6-15 feet high. The spring bud scales are large, jet-black, red, or yellow. As the white "pussies" break through these scales and open in early spring, they make a very attractive sight. A few days later the yellow anthers of the bloom turn them to yellow. The leaves are narrow.

These are hard to transplant but easy to start from cuttings. This bluestem is the most generally used of all native willows for ornamental planting. Stems of this and other willows are still used to make children's whistles.

Salix subcoerulea or *drummondii.* BLUE WILLOW, SILVER PUSSY WILLOW

A shrub 3-12 feet high, similar to the bluestem willow but found at higher altitudes from montane to subalpine zones. Stems smooth, purplish-brown to yellowish-lustrous with bluish "bloom." Leaves oblong, silvery-silky below, glabrous above. Anthers red.

Salix geyeriana. GEYER WILLOW

Found in the montane to subalpine zones, above 6,500 feet. Tall; twigs brown-purple to black when "bloom" is rubbed off. Leaves small and silky; buds small. Generally much like *S. bebbiana* but for the "bloom" on the twigs, which is more like *S. subcoerulea*

Sambucus pubens, bloom

Sambucus pubens, fruit

155

Sambucus coerulea glauca (p. 158)

Sarcobatus vermiculatus (p. 159)

Sarcobatus vermiculatus (p. 159)

Eleagnus angustifolia (p. 98)

Yucca harrimaniae (p. 172)

Spiraea caespitosa (p. 163)

Spiraea densiflora (p. 163)

Symphoricarpos oreophilus (p. 164)

Symphoricarpos occidentalis (p. 164)

Viburnum pauciflorum (p. 169)

Gaultheria humifusa (p. 103)

Sambucus coerulea (blue) *neomexicana*. NEW MEXICAN
BLUEBERRY ELDER (Spanish, CAPULIN SILVESTRE)

Occasionally found in moist, protected places in the montane
zone and foothills on the southern edge of the state. Grows as a
large shrub or small tree, from 6-12 feet high. Dark-brown, ridged
bark, with a large pith chamber in the center of the stem. Opposite, compound leaves. Flat heads of small, creamy-white flowers
in late spring, followed by heads of ¼ inch, blue-black berries with
a gray "bloom."

The berries are eaten by birds and humans. The plant is sometimes used as an ornamental shrub.

Sambucus coerulea glauca, BLUEBERRY ELDER (see page
156)

Lower and less tree-like than the New Mexican type. Plant,
flowers, and fruit rather attractive. Found occasionally in the
southwestern mountains, notably near Baxter Pass northwest of
Grand Junction.

Elderberries were eaten fresh or dried by the Indians, who also
used the stems to make flutes and clappers; the flowers were used
medicinally.

Sambucus melanocarpa. BLACKBEAD ELDER

Occasionally found in the mountains of the western slope,
apparently coming in from the west, or escaped from cultivation.
Compound leaves, erect stems, 4-6 feet high, with large yellowish-
brown pith. The bruised stems have a characteristic rank odor.
Round-topped heads of white flowers in late spring, followed by
blue-black berries which are eaten by birds or may be made into
jam and wine. They were often dried by the Indians.

This makes a good ornamental shrub as it extends its season of
bloom late into spring.

Sambucus canadensis. AMERICAN ELDER

Much like the blackbead elder but apparently coming into the
state occasionally from the northeast, possibly escaped from cultivation. They have large, flat-topped heads of white flowers and
black fruit. Stems 3-8 feet tall with white pith.

Sambucus pubens, microbotrys or *racemosa*. RED-BERRIED
ELDER, BUNCHBERRY ELDER

A very attractive small shrub of the subalpine and upper montane zones. Grows 2-4 feet high in moist places. Has large, com-

pound, opposite leaves, and pyramidal heads of small creamy-white flowers in late spring, followed by small, red berries. The berries are eaten by birds but are hardly palatable for human eating, sometimes considered slightly poisonous.

May be planted for ornamental use, but in a longer growing season, and with plenty of water in summer, it becomes a rank, sprawling shrub instead of the compact, attractive plant seen on the mountain hillsides.

Sapindus drummondii. WESTERN SOAPBERRY, CHINABERRY

A large shrub or small tree, sometimes up to 20 feet tall in our area. Coming into the state only in canyons and along streams in the southeastern corner. Red-brown, scaly, grooved bark. Compound leaves much like those of ash. Large, loose heads of tiny, white flowers and persistent berries, translucent, amber-colored, about ½ inch in diameter. Berries poisonous, containing saponin, but used by primitive peoples for making soap.

Sarcobatus (spiny flesh) *vermiculatus* (worm-like). BLACK GREASEWOOD (see page 156)

A coarse, desert shrub growing in dry, flat, alkaline places, generally over the southern and western part of the state at altitudes of 4,500-8,500 feet. It may grow from 2-8 feet tall with smooth, gray, thorny stems. The leaves are small and narrow, (1½ inches long or so), fleshy, twisted and salty-tasting. The flowers are inconspicuous, in small clusters, and the fruits consist of flat, round discs in clusters, usually green but sometimes pink or red. The bushes are browsed by starving cattle.

Senecio sp. OLDMAN, GROUNDSEL

At least two *Senecios* are woody at the base:

S. spartioides (grass-leaved) grows 8-24 inches tall, with linear leaves and upright heads of yellow bloom in September. Found throughout the state, except in the north, at 5,000 to 9,000 feet.

S. longilobus, FELTY GROUNDSEL, grows 1-3 feet high, is floccose-tomentose, has linearly-divided leaves and upright heads of yellow bloom. It is found on the southern plains of Colorado at 4,500-7,000 feet.

Shepherdia argentea, leaves and fruit

Shepherdia argentea, staminate bloom

Shepherdia argentea, pistillate bloom

Shepherdia canadensis, fruit

Shepherdia canadensis, bloom and leaves

160

Shepherdia rotundifolia,
staminate and pistillate bloom

Shepherdia rotundifolia

Shepherdia argentea (silver). SILVER BUFFALOBERRY

A tall, thicket-forming shrub, found largely along lower streams and bottoms on the western slope. Grows to 15 feet tall with opposite, thorn-tipped twigs. The leaves are willow-like and gray-silvery. The bright-red berries are borne in dense clusters. They are eaten by birds and, though too bitter to eat raw, they make excellent jelly. They contain so much pectin that several batches of jelly may be made from the same lot of berries.

Often called "squaw berries," they were used by Indians and pioneers to mix with stews, mush, and meat dishes, hence the name "buffaloberry."

Useful as a tall, ornamental shrub because of the interesting, gray foliage and bright fruit, but it may sucker out of bounds.

Shepherdia canadensis. RUSSET BUFFALOBERRY,
CANADIAN BUFFALOBERRY, BITTER BUFFALOBERRY

An interesting, low shrub in moist, well-drained places, largely beneath lodgepole pine, but extending up into the alpine zone and down to the upper foothills. Grows 2-4 feet tall as a well-shaped shrub. Covered in summer with oval leaves, dark gray-green above and silvery-webby below. Brown, scurfy scales on the buds and twigs and sparsely on the underside of the leaves. Underside of the leaves examined under at least 50 magnification appear covered with silvery cobwebs with tiny brown roses scattered throughout. The flowers, coming very early before the leaves, are tiny, yellow, with staminate and pistillate on separate plants, so only about half of the plants bear the small, red berries. These berries are relished by birds and may remain on the plant only a short time. They are too bitter for human use.

Since it grows naturally in well-drained, acid soil, this shrub is very difficult to transplant and grow under cultivation.

161

Shepherdia rotundifolia. SILVERLEAF or DESERT BUFFALOBERRY

A very attractive shrub of the Utah desert, probably coming into Colorado in a few canyons to the west. Roundish, thickish silvery-gray leaves on compact, fresh-looking shrubs. The blooms are tiny and yellow, coming early, staminate and pistillate on separate plants. Fruits are small "olives," silvery-wooly, hidden under the leaves.

This would make a wonderful cultivated shrub for dry places if propagation methods could be worked out.

Sorbus scopulina, bloom   Sorbus scopulina, bush

Sorbus scopulina or *sitenchis* or *Pyrus sambucifolia.* WESTERN MOUNTAIN ASH, GREENE'S MOUNTAIN ASH

A very attractive shrub, growing from 4-12 feet tall in moist places, mainly on the northern part of the western slope, but occasionally on the eastern slope from the foothills to the subalpine zone. It has large compound leaves. Bark on the twigs is yellow-brown, grading to dark-brown and gray on larger stems. Has an attractive "clean" appearance. Bears flat-topped heads of small white flowers in June, followed by bright, orange-red berries, about ⅓ inch in diameter, in October. The berries are very beautiful, eaten by birds but not very tasty for human use. The flowers have a peculiar, rancid odor. It has very attractive, red, fall coloring.

Has a heavy root system and is hard to transplant, but if moved when young, it makes a very nice, slow-growing shrub.

Spiraea caespitosa or *Petrophytum caespitosum.* TUFTED ROCKMAT, DWARF SPIREA, TURF SPIREA (see page 157)

A very interesting mat-plant of the western slope. Grows from cracks in ledges and forms mats a couple of inches thick which hang down over the vertical rocks or in the open, sometimes for 3-4 feet. These all seem to come from one long tap-root growing a long way back in the rock cracks. It has masses of very short, woody stems covered with small rosettes of tiny leaves. In summer there are heads of tiny, white flowers borne on 3 inch stems from each rosette of leaves. The leaves are gray-green, which gives the plant a most distinctive appearance. Some plants are very old and become a little larger each year.

It would be a very distinctive rock plant if it could be successfully propagated.

Spiraea (wreath) *lucida* (shining). SHINYLEAF SPIREA

A small shrub with erect stems, 1-3 feet high, possibly coming into the state from the north at elevations of 6,000-8,000 feet. It has birch-like leaves, 1-3 inches long, and small, white flowers in flat heads.

Spiraea densiflora. SUBALPINE SPIREA (see page 157)

A small, shrub somewhat similar to above, growing 1-1½ feet high, with procumbent stems, often in mat-like clumps. Possibly coming into the state from the north in the subalpine zone. Leaves ½-1 inch long; flowers rose-colored.

Stanleya pinnata. PRINCE'S PLUME

One of the most attractive plants in the mustard family. Found in alkaline soils on the desert, mesas and canyons of the southwest. Grows generally about 2 feet tall, but under favorable conditions will reach 3-4 feet. Often woody from the base up to a foot or so. Branched, pinnatifid, or simple leaves, sometimes remaining green over the winter. Tall, conspicuous, yellow plumes in summer.

Several other species are found over the state, but are not generally woody at the base. One has whitish plumes. Some are found at the head of canyons near limestone ledges, on the eastern slope, frequently in association with cut-leaf gaillardia. It is considered an indicator of calcium, gypsum and selenium in the soil.

163

Suaeda or *Dondia fruticosa* and *torreyana*. SEEPWEED, SEABLITE

A weed in the goosefoot family, found in alkaline soil, growing 10-25 inches tall, erect, branched, with small, linear, fleshy leaves. Woody at base. Found in western and southern Colorado at 4,500-7,000 feet. In fall it is conspicuous for its bright, rusty color against the white alkali.

Symphoricarpos **sp.,** bloom

Symphoricarpos occidentalis, bloom

Symphoricarpos oreophilus. MOUNTAIN SNOWBERRY (see page 157)

A small shrub, 2-5 feet high, growing in our higher foothills and mountains. Often found as a well-shaped specimen shrub, notably around Georgetown. Sometimes less formal and matted under trees. Slender, neat stems; leaves smooth, thin, oval. Berries attractive, clear-white, persistent. Flowers with tubes ⅓ to ½ inch long, pink and rather attractive.

This is one of the best native snowberries for cultivated use, though it does resent poorly-drained soil.

Symphoricarpos tetonensis. TETON SNOWBERRY

A similar shrub to *S. oreophilus*, with smaller flowers, occasionally found in the western half of the state.

Symphoricarpos utahensis. UTAH SNOWBERRY

A similar shrub found occasionally in the mountains of southwestern Colorado.

Symphoricarpos rivularis (brook-loving), *albus*, or *racemosus*. COMMON SNOWBERRY

The common snowberry of much of the United States. Found growing occasionally in the northwestern part of the state. Sometimes a rather scraggly shrub but may be developed into an attractive cultivated plant. It has tiny, pinkish flowers and large, persistent, white berries growing in clusters. Thin, oval leaves. Often grows over 3 feet tall.

Symphoricarpos albus (white) pauciflorus. DWARF SNOWBERRY

Somewhat similar to the common snowberry, but lower and thinner, with smaller fruits, growing solitarily or in pairs. Sometimes found in the foothills of central Colorado.

Symphoricarpos longiflorus.

Similar to S. albus but with longer flowers and narrower leaves. Occasionally found in extreme western Colorado.

Symphoricarpos vaccinioides or rotundifolius. WHORTLELEAF SNOWBERRY

A low shrub, about 2 feet high, found in the foothills and mountains of the western half of the state. The leaves are small, thick, rounded, and hairy. Not as well-shaped or attractive for cultivated use as the mountain snowberry.

Symphoricarpos rotundifolius. ROUND-LEAF SNOWBERRY

Similar to above, growing in western and south-central Colorado, on the mesas, along streams, and into the foothills.

Symphoricarpos palmeri.

A similar, trailing shrub of southwestern Colorado.

Symphoricarpos occidentalis. WESTERN SNOWBERRY, WOLFBERRY (see page 157)

Found mainly along the lower, larger stream banks and bottoms, in rich soil, over most of the state, except in the southwest. This has short, erect stems, 1½-3 feet high, somewhat branched above, in matted masses. Individual plants seldom seen, as it spreads quickly from underground runners. It bears very small, pinkish flowers followed by persistent clusters of round, dirty-white berries.

This is a wonderful soil binder and high ground cover for use along highways or other places.

Symphoricarpos orbiculatis (round) or *vulgaris* (common).
CORALBERRY, INDIAN CURRANT, MISSOURI
BUCKBRUSH

A low, spreading shrub associated with the snowberries, but bearing clusters of coral-red berries. Common over much of the east and much used as an ornamental, especially in shady places. Found occasionally here in the foothills, probably as an escape from cultivation.

Tamarix gallica (from France), *hispida*, or *pentandra*.
TAMARISK, SALT CEDAR (see page 176)

An attractive shrub which came originally from Europe or Asia but has rapidly naturalized itself along many of our larger streams at lower altitudes, notably the Colorado, Arkansas, and Dolores. Found over all desert areas along small washes where there is some underground moisture most of the year. Spreads so readily by its fine seed and likes our alkaline washes so well that thousands of acres of bottom land and streambeds are now covered with it on the plains of the east and roughlands of the southwest.

At first it has straight, erect stems, 4-8 feet high, an attractive red-brown; later it may become much branched, 10-15 feet high, scraggly, with dark colored stems. It has very small, light-green leaves which look much like juniper needles. It is covered most of the summer with large, terminal plumes of tiny flowers, dirty white to a very attractive pink. It forms a very deep root quickly, so it is able to grow in swamp land, extremely alkaline places, or even quite dry spots.

Because of the deep-rooting habit, older plants are very difficult to transplant, but it starts readily from pencil-sized cuttings. Selections with good color are planted as ornamentals all over the state. When used this way, the old wood should be cut out frequently, as the new wood is the most attractive.

Tetradymia canescens

Tetradymia (fourfold) *spinosa.* COTTONTHORN
HORSEBRUSH, SHORTSPINE HORSEBRUSH
A shrub 2-4 feet tall, found on dry hills and arid places of the
western slope. They are low-branching, with erect annual growth
from a woody base. Twigs and leaves covered with a hairy "wool"
which makes them stand out among green-leaved desert shrubs.
Flower heads bear a few stiff, wooly scales and a few small, yellow,
rayless, composite tube flowers, in May. Small, curved, spine-like
leaves.

Tetradymia canescens or *inermis.* SPINELESS GRAY
HORSEBRUSH, SMOOTH TETRADYMIA, FELT-THORN
Similar to *T. spinosa* but without definite spines and with
numerous, small, narrow leaves. Found on dry hills in the western
part of the state, up to 9,000 feet. May be rather attractive when
not too badly browsed.

Tetradymia nuttallii. NUTTALL HORSEBRUSH
A shrub somewhat similar to *T. spinosa,* found in the hills of
northwestern Colorado. The stems sometimes are smooth.

Thamnosma texana, montana or *texanum.* TEXAS DESERT
RUE, TURPENTINE-BROOM
A low shrub 4-15 inches tall, woody only at the base, occasionally found growing on dry land in the southwestern part of the
state. Strongly turpentine-like aroma at first, later more like
coconut. Closely related to the hoptree (*Ptelea*). The leaves are
short, linear, glaucous, green and glandular, falling early. The
branches are broom-like. Flowers small, yellow-purple, solitary,
and erect on the stems, in April and May. Fruits twin, sac-like,
pea-sized, bright yellow-green and gland-dotted, like miniature
oranges.

Vaccinium **sp.,** bloom   Vaccinium **sp.,** fruit

167

Vaccinium myrtillus (like myrtle) or *oreophilum.* MYRTLE
BLUEBERRY, MYRTLE WHORTLEBERRY, MOUNTAIN
BLUEBERRY, BLACK GROUSEBERRY, ROCKY
MOUNTAIN WHORTLEBERRY, HUCKLEBERRY

Common in upper montane and subalpine forests, often forming
almost a solid carpet for miles under spruce and fir trees. Grows
2-15 inches tall with brownish, (or yellowish-tinged red) angled
stems, spreading, not crowded. Leaves small, ⅓-1 inch long, oval,
smooth. Flowers tiny, waxy, pink and white bells. Berries blue-
black, smaller than those of dwarf bilberry, juicy, and very palatable, with a nut-like flavor. When the season is favorable, with
rains spaced right before ripening, these are very attractive fruits,
but one might travel for miles in some seasons and never see any.
Try gathering enough, sometime, to make a pie. The leaves have
been used to make a kind of tea.

V. membranaceum, THINLEAF HUCKLEBERRY; *V. occi-
dentale,* WESTERN HUCKLEBERRY; and *V. uliginosum,* BOG
BILBERRY, are listed by some authorities as being found here.

Vaccinium caespitosum (creeping). DWARF BILBERRY,
DWARF GROUSEBERRY, BLUEBERRY

A lower shrub than myrtle blueberry, sometimes covering the
forest floor in the subalpine zone, at 8,000-10,000 feet, on the
western slope. Spreading, with upright stems not strongly angled
as other species, but round or three-sided. Leaves ½-¾ inch long,
shiny. Flowers are ¼ inch waxy bells, white, pink, or red, in June.
Berries about ¼ inch in diameter, dark blue, edible, in the fall.

Vaccinium scoparium (of the rocks). BROOM HUCKLE-
BERRY, GROUSE WHORTLEBERRY, RED
BILBERRY, RED GROUSEBERRY, SMALL-LEAVED
BILBERRY

A small, dense shrub found growing in the montane and subalpine zones in the northern half of the state. Has slender, erect
stems, green and angled, crowded together in dense patches a few
inches tall. Bloom of tiny, waxy bells. Fruits are red berries,
smaller than those of the dwarf bilberry. Leaves less than ⅓ inch
long, thin and shiny. Eaten by many kinds of birds and wild animals, but of little value as browse for stock.

168

Viburnum pauciflorum (few-flowered) or *edule*. MOOSEBERRY VIBURNUM, SQUASHBERRY (see page 176)

A thin, straggling shrub with few low stems, 1-5 feet tall, found along small streams and in moist, shady places in the montane and into the subalpine zone. Not common or conspicuous. Leaves attractive, 3-lobed, maple-like, turning red in the fall. Occasionally there will be small, flat heads of small, white flowers. Fruits small, red, acid berries, seldom many to a head. These are edible but not tasty.

Viburnum lentago. NANNYBERRY VIBURNUM

This tall shrub may come into the state from the northeast. Some specimens have been reported near Boulder, but these may have been introduced. Large, oval leaves, flat heads of white flowers, and blue-black, edible berries.

Vitis vulpina (fox). WILD GRAPE, RIVERBANK GRAPE

Found growing occasionally along rivers and streams in the lower foothills of eastern Colorado. It requires good soil and water nearby to thrive. It is usually found climbing into shrubs or small trees or sprawling over rocks on stream banks. It may eventually grow vines 20 feet long or so, and an inch in diameter. The flowers are inconspicuous, growing in large heads, blooming early, fragrant. The leaves are 4-6 inches long, and palmately-lobed. The black grapes, which may be found in irregular clusters, are sometimes abundant and make wonderful jelly. They are also eaten by many birds and wild animals. It makes an attractive and ornamental vine for covering trellises and pergolas.

Other species that may be found occasionally in the state are:

Vitis doaniana, DOAN GRAPE, a vigorously-climbing vine, coming into the state from the southeast.

Vitis arizonica, CANYON GRAPE, a sprawly plant from the southwest.

Vitis longii, LONG'S GRAPE, a much-branched, sprawly plant occasionally found in the eastern part of the state, growing along streams.

Yucca baccata, fruit

Yucca baccata, curls

Yucca baccata, leaves

Yucca glauca, bloom

Yucca baccata (berried). INDIAN BANANA, (Spanish, PALMILLA, DATIL)

This yucca is found in southwestern Colorado on mesas and low hills at 5,500-7,500 feet. It has coarse, fleshy leaves, 1½-3 feet long, about 1½ inches wide, channelled, blue-gray-green. There are coarse, white, curled fibers along each edge of the leaves. The flowers are white "lilies," attached irregularly on short, crooked stems which hardly grow above the leaves. The fruits resemble and taste like cucumbers, being fleshy pods about 1¼ inches in diameter and 3-6 inches long, green or red-tinged. Occasionally these are shaped more like bananas, which gives the plant its name. They are edible if one is not too particular. They were commonly eaten by the Indians, raw or roasted. The young flower stems were also eaten like asparagus by the Indians, and even the flower petals were eaten. This species is dependent on the *Pronuba* moth for pollination, as are the others. The roots can be used for soap, but never were by the Indians, as there was a taboo against using or touching this species. The root system is quite different from all other species, consisting of a cluster of fleshy roots close up by the stems. These are easy to dig up and transplant for this reason, and are very valuable for ornamental use.

Although *Y. baccata* is often found growing with other yucca species, it very seldom hybridizes as the others frequently do.

Yucca glauca or *angustifolia*. SMALL SOAPWEED, SPANISH BAYONET, ADAM'S NEEDLE

Found commonly over the plains and into the foothills of the eastern slope at 4,000-8,500 feet. It may also be found in the foothills of the western slope, often hybridized with neighboring species.

The plants consist of dense clusters of stiff, sharp needles, parallel-veined, like giant evergreen leaves. They may be 1-2½ feet long and usually under ½ inch wide, with sharp needles on the points and ravelling threads on the edges. There is a rope-like root going straight down 1 to 3 feet from each plant, joining on to a large, 2 inch, fleshy, branched, horizontal storage root. There are also many small, red roots just under the surface which catch moisture from small rains and convey it to the storage root. These enable the plants to survive for many months without rain. The flowers are drooping, lily-like, cream-colored bells, 1¼ inches across when closed and 3 inches when open. They are on short stems attached to stalks 2-3 feet high that come from the center of the needle cluster. They open in the evening and are very beautiful. They can only be pollinated by the *Pronuba* moth, which lays its eggs in the flower ovaries. The seeds are round, black, and flat, stacked in the dry pods like pennies in a coin roll. The pods split open, dry, and turn brown, remaining on the stalks over the winter. They are used for dry arrangements.

This is a good evergreen ornamental where the sharp leaves are not objectionable. They were used by the Indians and cliff-dwellers for cordage to make rope, sandals, baskets, paint brushes and mats. The roots were pounded up to use as soap for washing hair and blankets. The buds, flowers, seeds, and emerging stalks were eaten raw or roasted, and used as a laxative. Thread and needle may be made from the leaves by stripping off the side fibers, leaving the end "needle" attached.

Many types and hybrids of *Y. glauca* are seen over the state which are very confusing and difficult to accurately identify.

Yucca harrimaniae. STUBBY-LEAF SOAPWEED, HARRIMAN YUCCA (see page 176)

An attractive dwarf yucca, found occasionally in southwestern Colorado at elevations of around 6,500 feet. It is more common in western Utah. Leaves are short, wide, often reflexed, densely-clustered, 6-8 inches long, ½-1 inch wide. The flowers are much like those of *Y. glauca*. The growing flower stalk, the white, lily-like flowers, and the dried seed pods are all very attractive.

Yucca angustissima (very narrow). FINELEAF YUCCA

A species of yucca occasionally found coming into the state from Utah and Arizona where it is common. The leaves are long, very narrow, fairly stiff, usually less than 50 in a bunch. The flower stalks often grow to 7 feet tall and are very ornamental. This is a distinct species, though there are frequent hybrids.

Yucca standleyi. STANDLEY YUCCA

This species is reported occasionally in the western and south-western part of the state at 5,000-7,500 feet. It is reported to have greenish-white flowers and rigid, linear, yellow-green leaves. It evidently has hybridized with several others so that it is not very distinct.

Yucca neomexicana mc elmo. SHORT-LEAF YUCCA

This is the common species over a large area in the extreme southwest corner of the state, but has never been recognized or named by the botanists. This same kind is found near Zuni, New Mexico. It and *Y. baccata* are the dominating kinds in the McElmo area. The needles are short, very narrow, stiff and clustered in bunches of 100, more or less. They spread from underground roots and so usually show a pattern on the ground following the roots in straight or crooked lines. The flowers are about 1¼ inches across, almost round, attached directly to a stem about 2-3 feet tall. They are very ornamental, white, and lily-like.

This has been classed by some as a type of *Y. harrimaniae, Y. glauca* or *Y. angustissima*, but it does not belong in any of these. It is a distinct type.

BOOKS FOR FURTHER REFERENCE

Recent:

Handbook of Rocky Mountain Plants, Ruth Ashton Nelson, 1969.

Edible Native Plants of the Rocky Mountains, H.D. Harrington, 1967.

Handbook of Plants of the Colorado Front Range, William A. Weber, 1953.

Manual of the Plants of Colorado, H.D. Harrington, 1964.

Plants of Rocky Mountain National Park, Ruth Ashton Nelson, 1953.

Flowers of the Southwest Mesas, Pauline M. Patraw, 1953.

Flowers of the Southwest Mountains, Leslie P. Arnberger, 1952.

Flowers of the Southwest Deserts, Natt N. Dodge, 1954.

Meet the Natives, M. Walter Pesman, 1952.

Healing Herbs of the Upper Río Grande, L.S.M. Curtin, 1948.

Older:

Trees and Shrubs of the Rocky Mountain Region, Burton O. Longyear, 1927.

New Manual of Botany of the Central Rocky Mountains, John M. Coulter, revised by Aven Nelson, 1909.

Rocky Mountain Flowers, Edith S. and Frederic E. Clements, 1914.

Northern Rocky Mountain Trees and Shrubs, Joseph E. Kirkwood, 1930.

Rocky Mountain Trees, Richard J. Preston, 1947.

Flora of Colorado, Per A. Rydberg, 1906.

Native Woody Plants of the United States, William R. Van Dersal, 1938.

Range Plant Handbook, U.S. Forest Service, 1937.

Desert Wild Flowers, Edmund C. Jaeger, 1944.

Flowering Plants and Ferns of Arizona, Thomas H. Kearney, Robert H. Peebles, and collaborators, 1942.

Standardized Plant Names, American Joint Committee on Horticultural Nomenclature, 1942.

Index

Photographs are indicated by *italicized page numbers* and are listed under Latin names only.

Buffaloberry, 161–62
Bull pine, 126
Bunchberry elder, 158
Bundle flower, 97
Bush cinquefoil, 128
Bush rock spirea, 105–6

Cactus, 97–98, 119, 120–21
Canadian buffaloberry, 161
Cañatilla, 100
Candelabra cactus, 120–21
Cane cactus, 120–21
Cañutillo del campo, 99
Canyon grape, 169
Capulín silvestre, 158
Cascade false azalea, 138
Cascades willow, 151
Cat's claws, 119
Ceanothus, 84, *84,* 85, *89*
Cedar, 110–11, 166
Celtis occidentalis, 85, *92*
Cercis occidentalis, 85, *92*
Cercocarpus, 86, *86,* 87
Cerro hawthorn, 95
Chamaebatiaria millefolium, 87, *109*
Chamiso, 80
Chamiso blanco, 90
Chamiso hediondo, 77–79
Cherry, 129–30
Cherrystone juniper, 108–10, 111
Chico, 80, 118
Chimaphila umbellata occidentalis, 87
Chinaberry, 159, *159*
Chinese matrimony vine, 118
Chokecherry, 87, 91, 131, 137
Chrysothamnus, 90, *109*
Cinquefoil, 128
Claret-cup cactus, 98
Clematis, 91, *91,* 93, 97
Cliff fendlerbush, 101
Cliff jamesia, 106
Cliffbush, 106
Cliffrose, 94–95
Coleogyne ramosissima, 93, *109*
Columbian rock clematis, 93
Compass plant, 98

Composite family, 104
Copperweed, 121
Coralberry, 166
Corkbark fir, 70
Cornus, 93, 93–94
Corylus, 94, 94
Cottonthorn horsebrush, 167
Cottonwood, 126–27
Covillea, 113
Cowania, 92, 94–95
Coyote willow, 154
Crataegus, 95, 95–96
Creeping juniper, 108
Creeping mahonia, 82
Creeping wintergreen, 103
Creosote bush, 113
Curl-leaf mountain mahogany, 86
Currant, 89, 142–44, 166

Dasiophora fruticosa, 128
Dátil, 170
Desert barberry, 81
Desert broom, 80–81
Desert buffaloberry, 162
Desert juniper, 111
Desert oak, 136–37
Desert rue, 167
Desert-thorn, 118
Desmanthus, 97
Devil's claw, 97
Ditaxis, 97
Doan grape, 169
Dogwood, 93–94, 148
Douglas fir, 118, 132
Douglas rabbit brush, 90
Dryad, 97
Dryas, 97
Dunebroom, 122
Dwarf ash, 103
Dwarf barrel cactus, 98
Dwarf bilberry, 168
Dwarf grouseberry, 168
Dwarf hairy ninebark, 124–25
Dwarf honey locust, 128
Dwarf juniper, 108
Dwarf maple, 70–71
Dwarf mistletoe, 118
Dwarf mountain laurel, 113

177

514 61▉